WRITING
VAMPYR

THE CRITERION COLLECTION

NEW YORK

Vampyr screenplay from *Four Screenplays*, translated
by Oliver Stallybrass, published by Secker &
Warburg. Reprinted by permission of The Random
House Group Ltd. Additional passages, translated
by Nicholas Elliott, from *Carl Th. Dreyer: Oeuvres
cinématographiques 1926–1934*, edited by Maurice
Drouzy and Charles Tesson.

Art direction: Sarah Habibi / Design: F. Ron Miller
Cover image: Michael Boland

First printing 2008

CONTENTS

INTRODUCTION

Carl Theodor Dreyer loosely based his film *Vampyr* on Irish Huguenot writer Sheridan Le Fanu's 1872 collection of supernatural tales *In a Glass Darkly*, and especially the story "Carmilla." But as this was far from a literal adaptation, and Dreyer chose to make his first sound film with very little dialogue, the screenplay he wrote with Christen Jul turned out to be a fascinating piece of writing in itself, a prose window into the Danish auteur's creative process. We present both "stories" here.

An earlier published English translation of the screenplay, by Oliver Stallybrass, was based on a version cut and slightly modified by Dreyer to more closely reflect the finished film. What follows is that translation but with the cuts reinserted and the alterations reversed to match the final draft of the original French screenplay, as published by Maurice Drouzy and Charles Tesson in *Carl Th. Dreyer: Oeuvres cinématographiques 1926–1934*: that is, Dreyer's final conception of the story, before the exigencies of location and budget (as well as some creative practical rethinking) came into play. We've marked the restored sections—excluding incidental language—in italics. These are mainly reinserted passages, but in a few cases, they represent substitutions, as in one very significant instance: the death scene of the doctor. In the film (and thus in the edited screenplay), the doctor dies in an abandoned factory; in the original screenplay, he dies in a bog. Another notable change from final screenplay to screen is a section recounting the vampire's control of a pack of dogs, which was cut during production, perhaps because Dreyer ultimately realized the difficulty in training dogs to act the parts as written. The final draft of the screenplay had some hand insertions and cross-outs by Dreyer. We've honored those late decisions. Occasionally, however, he deleted material but didn't offer substitutions. In these situations, in order to preserve the sense of certain passages (primarily in dialogue), we've retained what was crossed out but put those lines in brackets.

Following the screenplay is Le Fanu's "Carmilla." Le Fanu, born in Dublin in 1814, was a prolific writer across many genres; "Carmilla" is notable for introducing female vampires to that bloody literary tradition, the fundamental innovation that Dreyer adopts. It is fascinating to recognize the elements from which Dreyer built his narrative—the two young girls, the staking of the vampire's heart in the churchyard—and even more so to see how much he pared away. He moved the setting to contemporary France, for instance, thereby stripping the story of its Gothic quality. More importantly, in the story the friendship between the two girls is intense, erotic, and mysterious. But for his film, Dreyer drained away most of this psychological depth (and lesbian subtext), rendering the girls cinematic ciphers rather than fleshed-out characters. Where Carmilla is subtle, inscrutable, and manipulative, Léone is simply the puppet and victim of Marguerite Chopin—their relationship is not unlike that of actor to director. *Vampyr*'s continuing fascination rests in Dreyer's modernist, angular, and subjective take on the conventions of the vampire genre; "Carmilla" represents one of the earliest, and remains one of the best, inscriptions of the rules of what we now know as "the vampire story."

VAMPYR: THE SCREENPLAY

BY CARL THEODOR DREYER AND CHRISTEN JUL

A man is walking down the narrow riverside path that winds its way toward the spot where a ferry crosses to the other bank. It is a summer evening, after sunset. The traveler, Nikolas, is carrying a rucksack and, in his hand, a pair of fishing rods. He wants to spend his holiday in solitude, which is why he has come to this remote region in search of peace.

He arrives at the old inn and finds the door closed. The inn is lying in profound silence, as if all its occupants have gone to bed. Nikolas rattles at the door, but it is well and truly locked. At this moment he sees a reaper walking along with his scythe over his shoulder. He looks at the man curiously as he walks down toward the ferry. He shouts after him:

Hullo, you there!

But the reaper, not hearing his cry, continues on his way. The landscape is bathed in a gray, dim twilight; every object has a tinge of unreality.

Nikolas goes round to the back of the house. There he discovers a window in which a light can be seen. He comes nearer, knocks on the windowpane, and listens;

but not a sound reaches him. Simultaneously the light goes out. Nikolas knocks again. Silence still. But now a window is opened quietly on the floor above, and a timid child's voice asks:

Who's there?

Nikolas runs his eye up the facade of the house and discovers a little girl of thirteen with a gentle, frightened face. She says to him:

I'll come down and open the door.

She gestures, indicating that he is to go to the front door. Then she carefully closes the window.

As Nikolas stands waiting, he glances down in the direction of the ferry. The ferryman—who has a white beard—boards the ferryboat, which begins crossing the river. He goes backward and forward, pulling laboriously at the iron chains that run rattling and squealing round the ungreased wheels.

Meanwhile the little girl has opened the door of the inn. She is a strange child. She looks rather small for her age and wears spectacles. Her eyes are moist, as if she has just been crying. When she talks to somebody, she tilts her head backward.

Nikolas enters, and the girl shuts the door behind him. He slips his rucksack from off his shoulders. As he is doing so, a door opens a few inches and a face appears, staring inquisitively. The little girl gives a sign to Nikolas to follow her up the stairs leading to the guest rooms. She lights a candle in a little enamel candlestick of the kind found in country districts and hands him the candlestick.

On the floor above, the doors out onto the passage are standing open. The rooms are poorly furnished, the beds without bedclothes, the windows dirty, as if they have not been cleaned for a long time. The little girl conducts Nikolas to a Spartanly furnished room. On a table he finds a candlestick with a half-used candle, beside which are lying another candle and a box of matches. He lights the candle. The girl, who has remained standing in the doorway, says with an inclination of the head:

Good night, sir!

NIKOLAS: Good night!

The girl disappears and shuts the door behind her. He glances round the room. Over the bed hangs one of those copperplate engravings, framed in glass, that are so common in the country. Nikolas looks at the engraving for a moment. Then from a neighboring room he hears a woman sobbing. He opens the door a few inches and unintentionally listens to what follows. The weeping stops, then starts again. A man's voice is heard trying to calm the woman, but she is incapable of mastering her despair. She breaks out:

> Oh, my little boy! Why did he have to die—why should I have to lose him . . . why, why?

> MAN'S VOICE (consolingly): Don't cry!

> WOMAN'S VOICE (in despair): I cannot live without him . . . My little boy, my little boy!

The weeping eases off.

> WOMAN'S VOICE: Oh God, oh God!

We hear a door opening, followed by footsteps; then everything is quiet again. Nikolas, who had lifted the candle to look at the engraving, puts it down and, after locking the door, crosses to the window to pull down the blind. First, however, he looks out across the river, where he sees the reaper with the scythe sitting on the railing of the ferryboat, while the ferryman still goes monotonously backward and forward—like the ferryman on the river separating life and death. Then Nikolas draws down the blind. It is one of those blinds, often seen in the country, that have some painted motif: a temple, a forest, or the like. Then he sets his watch. The sound of the watch being set continues during the following shot, which shows the shadow of the house creeping slowly over the ground—a symbol of time passing.

A moment later we return to the room. Nikolas has been asleep for some time. Somewhere in the house a clock strikes eleven; then we hear the footsteps of somebody approaching and knocking on the door: two knocks—and again two knocks. In his deep sleep Nikolas seems to hear the knocking without taking it in fully. He reacts while still half asleep, turns his head toward the door, and sees the handle slowly turning. Then the door is opened, inch by inch, as if by an invisible hand. A man enters the room, wearing a full-length dressing gown. Without a sound he approaches the bed and leans over Nikolas.

Are you asleep?

Almost unconsciously Nikolas opens his eyes and meets the stranger's inquiring gaze.

Wake up!

Nikolas looks at him in astonishment and asks, almost in a whisper:

Who are you?

The stranger, whose whole bearing and behavior indicate unease and nervousness, straightens up, crosses the room, pulls up the blind, and stands so that the moonlight falls on his face, which shows traces of recent suffering. He takes out a handkerchief and mops his brow with a nervous movement . . . like a man dreading a catastrophe. Suddenly he raises his head and listens closely. Then he says:

Shh!

Nikolas looks at him in growing amazement. The stranger continues to stand there, as if his thoughts are somewhere quite apart. Then he seems to remember where he is and why he has come. He again goes right up to the bed and leans over Nikolas. In broken syllables he stammers out the words:

She mustn't die . . . Do you hear? . . .
She's dying, she's dying!

The stranger speaks like a man in dire need, one who in his agony doesn't know where to turn for help. Suddenly— without a transition—he turns away and crosses to the door. There he stops, apparently absorbed in his own thoughts. Absently he raises a thumb to his lips, looks at it, and licks it. Then he puts a hand in his dressing-gown pocket and takes out a parcel the size of a book. He puts the parcel down, takes his leave with a polite inclination of the head, and goes out.

Nikolas sits half up in bed, tormented by doubt. Has he been dreaming? Has there really been anybody in his room? He lights a match and looks at his watch. It is five past eleven. Then he gets up, goes to the door, and tries it; it is firmly locked. He looks at the blind; the blind is up. And on the table lies the parcel. Some words are written on it:

To be opened after my death!

Nikolas is unable to go back to sleep. A dying man has called on him. He cannot ignore this call! He must go and look for the man who has asked for help. He starts putting his clothes on.

Outside, the shadow of the inn creeps farther and farther over the ground—time is passing.

Nikolas has crept stealthily down the stairs and

stolen out of the door without waking the people in the inn. The moon is shining, so that everything is clearly visible. He takes a few steps, then stops irresolutely. Which way shall he go? It is, in truth, a hopeless task that he has undertaken, since this stranger has given him no information whatsoever. As he stands like this, he suddenly catches sight of a shadow gliding down the white road. It is the shadow of a man—a man with a wooden leg—followed by the shadow of a dog. Nikolas stands stock-still for a moment, utterly bewildered. Yes, it quite definitely is a shadow—and only a shadow. There is no man or dog to be seen. The man's shadow stops, turns slowly, and looks all round. With mounting astonishment Nikolas watches to see what will happen next.

The man's shadow walks on and joins a group of other shadows engaged in digging a grave in the shadow of a tree. We see these shadows of grave diggers as they dig their shovels deep in the earth and throw up shadows of shovelfuls onto a heap of earth that likewise is a shadow. One of the shadows in the grave stops when the shadow of the man with the dog comes up to him. After a short conversation between the two men, the shadow of the man with the dog turns, takes a few paces in the direction whence he came, and beckons to somebody.

Nikolas looks in the same direction and sees a weird procession: two men's shadows, sharply outlined against the light road, walking slowly along, carrying a dead body. The limply hanging arms and dangling legs show clearly that it is a human body. The whole procession of shadows is utterly fantastic. Nikolas follows the happenings with the keenest attention: the shadow of the man with the dog gives an order; they start laying the body in the grave; then the shadow of the man with the dog moves away.

Nikolas has an impulse to follow this shadow. A voice inside him tells him that there must be some connection between the apparition in the room of the inn and this phenomenon of the shadows. He follows the shadow, which suddenly leaves the road and disappears through a door or opening in the wall of a factory. This factory is, strictly speaking, only the ruins of a factory that has been derelict for many years. Half of the windowpanes are broken, and those remaining are covered in dirt and cobwebs. The tumbledown factory looks dismal and fantastic in the moonlight and makes one think of a gigantic churchyard.

Nikolas enters the factory by the same opening through which the shadow disappeared. The room Nikolas enters is a small, bare, square room, full of rubble and stones, through which Nikolas carefully threads his way. There are two doors. Nikolas tries one, which leads into a room with no other exit; then he opens the other and comes into a room with another door. When Nikolas opens this

latter door, he finds a steep staircase behind it. Nikolas
treads gingerly on the stairs to see if they creak; then
he goes up the stairs. When he reaches the top, he finds
himself facing another door. Just as he is about to open
this, he hears through the door footsteps echoing over
the tiled floor. Nikolas stands rooted to the spot. The
steps come nearer, and as they do so we see under the
door a steadily increasing shaft of light. He can hear that
they are the footsteps of a man. He watches the door as
if hypnotized. The man on the other side has stopped;
now the door handle moves, and a key is turned. Then
the footsteps die away.

Nikolas, who has hardly dared to draw breath for
fear of giving himself away, tries the door handle. To
his surprise the door opens. The man, whose steps can
no longer be heard, has evidently unlocked the door for
an expected visit. Nikolas opens the door wide and goes
in. He finds himself in a room resembling a corridor.
A little way along there is a door. Nikolas tiptoes up to
it and opens it. The room into which it leads is empty.
Nikolas is about to turn back into the corridor when he
hears a door slam. He peeps out through the partly open
door. There now enters, by the door through which he
himself has passed a moment ago, an old woman of erect
bearing who holds her head high and proudly. She must
be very old. Her skin is pale as wax, yellowish, and drawn

tight over her cheekbones. Her movements are stiff and resolute; she supports herself on a stick, which strikes the tiles with sharp, regular clicks. The old woman is blind. Her eyes are covered with a film and have a dead look. Her lips are thin. Her whole face bears the stamp of cruelty.

The moonlight shines through the window, outlining its cruciform frame sharply on the floor or the wall. When the blind woman reaches the window, she opens it with her stick before continuing on her way, and the shadow of the cross disappears. She goes through the door behind which Nikolas has hidden, and he decides to follow her. Suddenly she stops, throws her head back, and sniffs the air like a dog. Nikolas stops too. She turns abruptly and says:

Who's there?

Nikolas waits as quiet as a mouse. The blind woman is reassured and walks on. Nikolas follows. But at the first turn of the corridor she vanishes. *Then suddenly Nikolas hears an infernal noise that must be coming from a neighboring room. He moves in the direction of the noise and beholds a strange spectacle through a dusty window covered in spiderwebs. He sees a pack of dogs running to and fro in a vast room, yelping, barking, growling.*

A pack of wild and untamed-looking beasts . . . Then the blind woman enters. She steps forward among the dogs, and they gather around her. Now she holds out her walking stick. The dogs lie down. They grovel before her and wag their tails. Only one dog, a bigger and more savage-looking one than the others, leaps at her. She leans toward him and whispers something in his ear. The dog barks loudly, as if to show he has understood, then jumps into the pile. Surrounded by all these barking, howling dogs squeezing together to get as close as possible to her, the blind woman crosses to a door at the far end of the vast room and opens it. The dogs rush forward like a pack of hunting dogs set upon its prey.

Nikolas stands speechless for a moment. Then another remarkable thing happens. A sound that has no connection with the preceding scene reaches his ear. It is the sound of music, and the tune being played has a dancing rhythm, faintly reminiscent of a slow mazurka. Nikolas listens for a second, then takes a few steps in the direction of the sound and turns into a corridor, at the end of which there is a door. When he opens this, it is as if the music, cooped up behind the closed door, now rushes at him like a wave falling back to its original level. The music seems to come from some apertures in the wall. They are like organ pipes; at all events the music swells from them as from an enormous organ. The same blind woman now appears in a corner of the room. She stops. She makes a sign with her stick, and the music stops.

From the opposite corner of the room a curious figure now comes toward her: a lame man as thin as a beanstalk. But in spite of his lameness he moves with great agility; he looks remarkably like a giant wading bird. Involuntarily he uncovers his head and holds his hat in his hand while talking to the blind woman. She gives him a curt order and walks on, finally disappearing in the factory's labyrinth of passages and corridors.

The one-legged man went . . . [This sentence was left incomplete in the final manuscript. —Ed.] A man comes up to him. They whisper together. The new arrival is an unpleasant character with pig's eyes, a flat nose, a low forehead, and sparse, stiff bristles. He has an underhung jaw and a powerful chin. There is something bestial about his appearance. The two men walk over to a window niche, where a man is lying asleep on the floor, huddled up like a dog. As the one-legged man wakes the sleeper with a kick from his wooden leg, the man with the pig's eyes pulls out his knife and tests the cutting edge with his thumb. The sleeper has sharp features and a hardened expression, as if his face has been carved in wood. As he gets up, he scratches his unshaven cheek with a bent forefinger. Then all three disappear.

At appropriate times, the scenes described above are

interrupted by very short images of the unleashed dogs following the lead dog across the fields until they reach the top of a hill in the moors where a flock of sheep graze under the supervision of a twelve- or fourteen-year-old shepherd. Long before the dogs get there, we can hear their yapping and barking. Suddenly they appear on the hill. The terrified shepherd runs off. In the few shots that follow, we see that the dogs have surrounded the poor shepherd and that they are forcing him to move in a certain direction.

Nikolas exits the factory. He is walking along the road when the silence of the night is shattered by the dogs barking and the child's piercing cries. The young shepherd comes running, terror-stricken, with his arms extended before him. He yells out in great distress, for the wild dogs are coming behind him, running grouped in a semicircle that dictates the fugitive's direction. They lead him to a little house, an old, deserted dwelling with windows that have been painted over white and that in the moonlight resemble glass eyes.

Nikolas dashes to help him. The boy has reached the door that leads to a courtyard behind the house. The dogs are drawing closer and closer. Nikolas hears them rushing and panting in their savage chase. But he doesn't reach the door quickly enough to seize the child, who has stopped, terrified, then turned around and, with his back to the door, is trying to push it open to escape from the furious dogs. Then the door opens, as if by the work of an invisible hand. The boy races in, and the yapping pack of dogs sweeps in behind him. When Nikolas reaches the door, it has closed again and will not open, no matter how hard he pounds or kicks at it. He runs to the house's main door. He knocks. No answer! The wire to the doorbell has disappeared, but all the way at the top, at the corner of the door frame, he notices the bend that leads the wire to the bell. He pulls on it. The doorbell rings. Still no answer! He tries the handle and finds that the door is open.

He enters a corridor. There is a smell of mold. Everything is old, dirty, and dilapidated. Dust and cobwebs in every corner. Perhaps inhabited, perhaps not, very little furniture. An old cupboard, a chair, an umbrella lacking its cover, a greasy hat on a hatrack. In the corridor there is a door with reinforced panes of glass; the corridor leads to a staircase descending to the gloomy depths of a cellar. There is a deathlike hush in the house.

Is there anybody here? asks NIKOLAS
in a loud voice.

No answer. The silence seems even deeper after the sound of his own voice. Opposite the staircase a door is standing ajar. Nikolas opens it cautiously. The room he looks into is peculiar in the extreme. *One has the impression it is both a common room and a medical consulting room.* It is depressingly untidy and dirty. Collections of eggs, birds, and mussel shells, distilling flasks and glasses of all sizes, dusty and filthy, some spiders under glass cases, a doctor's scales with weights the color of verdigris, books, apothecary's glasses containing leeches and other crawling things. The skeleton of a child. A parrot on its perch. But not a single living human being.

Nikolas goes through a door into another room. As he does so he gets the feeling that there must have been people here quite recently. In the middle of the floor stands a black wooden coffin on two wooden trestles. On the floor, wood shavings and bricks; on the window ledge, a bowl of dirty water, soap, a brush, and a comb; and standing against the wall, a saw and other carpenter's tools. Nikolas goes through this room in turn. The house's inhospitable atmosphere is beginning to oppress him; he has the feeling that he is not alone, even if the room is empty. He walks on tiptoe, looks all round, and opens and closes the doors cautiously.

The third room is completely empty. Dust is lying so thick that it muffles the sound of his footsteps. Flakes of plaster are lying on the floor; they have peeled off from the wall and ceiling, on which there are rusty stains made by the rain dripping from the leaky roof. In the window there is a potted plant hanging, withered, from its stake.

Facing him, a door. This leads into a room *where the darkness is even deeper than in the other rooms. The floor is tiled, which makes the echo sound harsh and cold.* Some large boxes bar his way. Then he suddenly thinks he sees, directly opposite, a long corridor opening out of a wall with no door in it. *He sees someone there moving away from him. It's the old blind woman from the factory. He tries to rapidly bypass anything barring him from catching up with her. At the same moment, she goes around the corner at the other end of the corridor. She disappears before Nikolas reaches the entrance, after having cast a glance at him over her shoulder.* When he reaches it, there is no entrance after all, but an uninterrupted wall, into which he has bumped; he lights a cigarette, by the light of which he sees that he is standing close up against a whitewashed wall that is split, cracked, and full of mold. He turns round and discovers that he is now in an old laundry room. It has not been used since time immemorial. Everything is covered in dust. On the copper are standing some rusty birdcages and mousetraps. Old paraffin lamps are lying in a heap on the floor. But what astonishes Nikolas most is a collection of children's clogs standing neatly in rows. They are not quite as dusty as the other things in the old laundry room.

But all of this hasn't put him on the trail of the boy he wanted to help. For this reason he goes through the empty room and back to the spot where a door leads out to the staircase. There he stops, and now he hears—in the quivering stillness of the old house—a child weeping. Then a scream, a half-suppressed child's scream, as if a hand had closed over the mouth of the screamer.

It comes from the cellar, but just as Nikolas is about to descend, he hears steps on the staircase above. Somebody is coming down. He sees only this person's hand, as it fumbles its way slowly down the handrail. He can only guess at the owner of the hand. The hand continues to glide down, and Nikolas, summoning all his courage, says:

Good evening!

But the hand only rises and gestures to him to be quiet. The person stops on the staircase. Not a sound. Then the hand resumes its downward gliding movement. Nikolas realizes that it is the hand of an old man. The figure continues down to the landing, and Nikolas takes a few steps toward him. He sees that it is a slender, elderly man. His hair hangs in tangled wisps. He pokes his head forward in an attentive attitude. He is wearing spectacles, and his face is marked by unctuous servility, coupled with

relentless malignity. He looks like a usurer. This man is
Marc. At this moment everything about him indicates that
he is listening.

NIKOLAS: I . . .

But Marc interrupts him with a violent movement and
bids him be quiet.

MARC: Shh!!!

He continues to the staircase leading down to the cellar,
descends two steps, and leans over the handrail—we see
his neck—and stands there for a long time listening as
he leans toward the depths. Then he comes back up to
Nikolas, and his gaze is fixed and tense.

MARC: Did you hear? . . .

NIKOLAS: Yes, the child . . .

But now Marc's bearing changes. He looks as if he has
woken from the hypnotic state that his intense interest in
the cellar has induced. He suddenly becomes aware that
he has found a stranger on his private staircase. His face
clouds over with suspicion.

MARC (sharply): The child?

NIKOLAS: Yes.

MARC: There's no child here.

NIKOLAS: But . . . the dogs . . .

During this exchange [Marc] has more or less pushed Nikolas before him to the front door, without ever actually touching him. But his intention is clear enough.

MARC: There's no child here, and no dogs either.

NIKOLAS: No?

MARC: No! (Opening the front door) Good night!

NIKOLAS: Good night! . . .

Marc has succeeded in getting rid of Nikolas, and without further comment he shuts the door.

Nikolas stands irresolutely for a moment outside the door, while he reflects on his visit to this extraordinary house. Then he sets off slowly down the road, until at a turn in the road he catches sight of the three disembodied shadows that took their orders in the factory from the blind woman. The group is recognizable by the man with the wooden leg. Nikolas follows the three shadows, feeling instinctively that they will lead him to the man who has asked him for help.

In the house, meanwhile, Marc has turned back to the stairs. From the depths of the cellar he hears steps approaching and the sound of a stick striking the ground; with great servility he greets the blind woman as she comes up the stairs.

Marc follows her with exaggerated and ill-placed attentiveness. He opens for her the door into the consulting room and closes it behind her. The blind woman continues on her way without taking any notice of him. Her head is tilted back slightly, as is often done by blind people. She moves forward, cold and unbending. As she crosses the consulting room, she is on the point of stumbling over a large book lying open on the floor. Marc kicks it hurriedly aside and draws up a chair for her at the table. She ignores him completely. When she sits down, he takes her stick and puts it carefully on the table. She is sitting. Marc stands motionless and expectant. Then she slowly takes a medicine bottle from her pocket. With her bony hand she holds it out to Marc. When he takes it, she raises her face toward him for the first time. He looks at her; they appear to exchange a conspiratorial glance: an order is given and received.

At this moment an explosion of laughter is heard from the parrot. Marc tears off his spectacles—which rest a little way down his nose—polishes them, and gives the parrot a nearsighted, malicious, and knowing look.

Then he goes to a shelf on which he places the medicine bottle. *He places the bottle just beneath a spider's thread, by which the spider climbs to a web hanging freely beneath the ceiling.*

Out of the spiderweb comes the image of the castle's facade. The camera moves to a certain window on the ground floor of the castle, behind which we see a man getting up and taking a lamp. This is the man who, at the inn, visited Nikolas in a dream. We can call him Bernard. He leaves the room.

A shot of the road, where we see Nikolas following the three shadows.

THE INTERIOR OF THE CASTLE

Bernard enters a room arranged as a sickroom. A woman is lying there in bed; it is his daughter, whose name is Léone. A nurse is looking after her. Léone is a woman of twenty-six. *Her cheekbones are quite high, yet this does not disrupt the harmony of her face . . . Her nose is well formed, her eyes almond-shaped.* She is very pale, as if suffering from anemia. Bernard goes up to the bed.

The nurse stands beside him and says:

The wounds are very nearly healed!

Bernard holds the lamp so that the light falls on Léone's throat. In the middle of her throat, where the jugular vein shows blue under the white skin, we see two small marks, reminiscent of those that appear after a cat or rat bite. There have been two wounds, but they are now closing and healing. Bernard prepares to go; he turns in the door because Léone, his eldest daughter, has stirred. She moves her lips as if in a horrible dream, and her face takes on an expression of terror. She stammers out, like a person speaking in her sleep:

The blood! . . . The blood! . . .

Then she seems to calm down. Bernard goes back to the bed. Léone seems to wake up; she opens her eyes, recognizes her father, gives him a feeble smile, and takes his hand. Then her hand falls back down. Bernard looks at her with intensely serious eyes. It is evident that even if he does not know the cause of her condition, he has his suspicions about it. He takes a last look at his daughter and goes. In the door he turns to the nurse.

BERNARD: You mustn't lie down and go to sleep until
the doctor has been here!

The nurse promises not to do so. As the nurse closes the
door, Léone moves again. The nurse watches her closely.

THE ROAD
*The three shadows disappear in the shade from the high
wall surrounding the castle. Their disappearance happens
in such a manner that Nikolas does not know whether
they've continued to the right or to the left. He remains
indecisive for a moment.*

THE CASTLE
Léone's sickroom. The nurse puts a chair by the bed.
*Léone is not asleep. She appears to be fighting to stay
awake.*
The nurse says:

You must sleep now!

LÉONE *(shaking her head): No!*

NURSE: *Why not?*

LÉONE: *I'm scared!*

NURSE: *Of what?*

LÉONE: *I don't know!*

The nurse fixes her pillow.

THE GROUNDS OF THE CASTLE

Nikolas jumps up on the wall ringing the castle. When he appears on the wall, his body forms a ghostly silhouette against the night sky (to suggest the shadows he is pursuing).

THE COURTYARD

The three shadows emerge from the shadow of the trees, steal across the moonlit courtyard, and disappear into the deep shadows of the castle.

THE CASTLE

Bernard in the corridor, outside the door of his room. He still has the lamp in his hand. He goes into his room.

THE COURTYARD

Enter Nikolas (from another direction than the three shadows we saw in an earlier shot). He finds himself under the room that Bernard has just entered. Through the lighted window he sees Bernard putting down his lamp and recognizes him as the man who visited him in his dreams. At the same moment he sees the three shadows going diagonally across the ceiling of the room; at that moment Bernard leaves the window and goes across to a bookshelf. Nikolas rushes to the main door of the castle. He rings vigorously at the door. The bell gives a feeble ring. The echo dies away, and everything is quiet again. Nikolas rings again. Now he hears behind the door an old person's shuffling steps. He tugs at the door and shouts:

Open up . . . open up quickly . . . hurry!

The door remains closed, but inside he hears a voice.

Who is it?

NIKOLAS: For God's sake . . . hurry . . .
they're killing him! . . .

Then the door opens, but only a few inches. Through the chink we see old Joseph, a faithful manservant. He is wearing only trousers and a shirt, which is open at the neck. His braces are hanging down his back. He is carrying a lamp in his hand. The manservant wants to know more, but at this very moment a long, drawn-

out scream is heard, hideous and horrifying. For a
moment this scream seems to paralyze the two men. The
manservant puts his hand to his mouth in order not to
scream himself. Mechanically he opens the door wide.
The two men rush into the house.

THE LANDING OUTSIDE LÉONE'S ROOM

The nurse opens the door in terror. Her facial contortions
show that the invalid has heard nothing but that, on the
other hand, she dare not leave her either.

THE DRAWING ROOM ADJOINING
THE ROOM WHERE THE MURDER
HAS TAKEN PLACE

The manservant and Nikolas try to open the door into
Bernard's room, but the body of the dying man is lying
just behind it, preventing them from opening it more
than a few inches. The dying man's screams fill them
with horror.

JOSEPH: The other door!

He gives Nikolas the lamp and hurries out to the other
entrance to the room containing the dying man. When
the manservant goes into the room, he finds his master
slumped up against the door, with one hand still clutching

the door handle convulsively, as if trying to escape the lethal weapon that struck him just as he reached the door. His screams give way to gasps, and he has difficulty in breathing. The manservant kneels behind him to pick him up. Nikolas has put the lamp on the piece of furniture nearest the door. Now he comes up, and at a sign from the manservant makes the murdered man release his grip on the door handle. The dying man tries desperately to open his eyes and speak. Then it grows quiet, and in the silence only his labored breathing can be heard. Suddenly he gives a deep sigh, at the same time opening his eyes and looking frantically around. He looks up at Nikolas. An expression of surprise lights up his face for a moment. The manservant has intercepted this look and glances curiously at Nikolas. But the dying man's stare again becomes fixed and glassy. He stammers:

Water!

Nikolas gets up; on a table he finds a tray with cups and a jug of linden tea. He pours out a little tea in a cup, which he lowers to the dying man. With a teaspoon he moistens the dying man's lips.

While Nikolas has been occupied with the tray, an old serving woman has arrived at the door connecting the death room with the drawing room. It is the housekeeper of the castle, the wife of the old manservant; they tell her to come in by the other door. She enters with the chambermaid. Each woman carries a lamp that she puts down at random. The old housekeeper moves her hands incessantly under her motley apron.

On the landing, the nurse is still standing, terror-stricken, outside the open door of Léone's room, listening and staring out into the darkness. Then Gisèle appears, wearing an apronlike dress, the sleeves of which are gathered in a tight band round her wrists. A very simple and slightly old-fashioned dress that can easily be turned into a kimono. Her hair hangs loose. She thinks the scream has come from the sickroom and is surprised to find the nurse on the stairs.

GISÈLE: Wasn't it here?

NURSE: No, it's down there.

The nurse listens for sounds in Léone's room, while Gisèle runs down the stairs.

THE ROOM OF THE MURDER
Enter Gisèle. She stops dead by the door, paralyzed by the sight of her father lying on the point of death. She looks at the chambermaid and the old housekeeper, who

are clinging to each other, while tears run down their cheeks. She desperately looks at the three lamps and wrings her hands. Beside herself, and with eyes dilated with terror, she goes to her father and kneels by his side. He understands that she is there. His face lights up for a moment, after which he closes his eyes again for a while, as if trying to draw breath for the few words he wants to say; but he has not sufficient strength left. [He uses his last ounce of strength to draw a ring from his finger. He hands the ring to Gisèle, who recognizes it. It is a signet ring, the signet of which is formed like a tiny gold cross.] She holds it in the hollow of her hand, while her eyes fill with tears. The dying man catches Gisèle's eye and, as it were, guides it over to Nikolas, as if to say: "This man will protect you." His gaze becomes vacant, without consciousness, fixed and glassy. His breathing comes in jerks. Nikolas tries to moisten his lips, but the liquid runs down his chin and thence onto his breast. His teeth are firmly clenched, and the corners of his mouth are sagging. The brief death struggle has begun. While we see the little group by the door, which has been joined by the old coachman, we hear the dying man's death rattle. Tears run down the coachman's furrowed cheeks.

ON THE LANDING

The nurse is still standing there. The death rattle reaches

her ears. She goes into Léone's room and shuts the door behind her.

THE DEATH ROOM

Here the silence of death prevails. The group by the door follows with bated breath the last spasms of the death struggle. Now the murdered man is drawing his last gasp. The old housekeeper goes up to Gisèle, who is no longer weeping but merely stares uncomprehendingly at her father's lifeless body. The old housekeeper calls to her gently. Gisèle looks at her in surprise.

Is he dead? she asks.

The old woman nods. Gisèle looks once more at her father's face, then bursts into tears and, without offering any resistance, lets herself be led across to the wall, where she collapses into a chair, throwing her arms round the old woman and clinging to her hand. She says nothing. She only weeps and weeps. The coachman goes out.

Nikolas and the manservant carry the dead man across to a sofa. As this takes place, we hear Gisèle sobbing. While the manservant is still in the room, Nikolas goes up to Gisèle. He helps the maid to lead Gisèle away. The latter is led out unresisting. He takes her by the arm. She hides her face in her hands and weeps heart-rendingly. The manservant remains in the room. He walks round in a curiously restless way; he makes a number of unconscious movements with his hands, as if wanting to make somebody or other keep quiet.

THE COURTYARD

The coachman crosses the courtyard, opens the door of the carriage entrance, and draws out a hunting carriage. He pulls it slowly and carefully, as if wanting to muffle the sound.

THE DRAWING ROOM

The old housekeeper has gone on ahead in order to light a lamp. Nikolas gets Gisèle to sit down. Her gaze is vacant, and her lips tremble as she attempts to suppress her sobbing.

Nikolas walks to and fro in this antechamber of death, deeply disturbed by the scene he has just witnessed. As he reaches the door, the old housekeeper is standing in front of him.

HOUSEKEEPER (in a low voice):
Couldn't you stay here?

Nikolas replies with a movement of his head, then continues to pace the floor.

THE COURTYARD
The coachman leads a horse from the stable.

THE DRAWING ROOM
Nikolas stops in front of Gisèle's chair and looks compassionately at her. She is sitting as motionless as a statue. Only her lips are trembling, as if she is praying quietly. Suddenly she senses his presence. She looks up at him imploringly and says in a voice choked with tears:

More light!

He takes out some matches and lights the lamps on an old piano, which is covered with a faded green silk cloth. The only sound is the monotonous ticktock of an old clock, which suggests the dull beating of an almost exhausted heart.

THE COURTYARD
The coachman is hitching the horses.

THE DRAWING ROOM
Nikolas lights another lamp, and as he puts out the match he looks at Gisèle. She is sitting with her hands in her lap, rocking her head backward and forward. Her eyes are glazed. She is doing all she can to prevent herself

from breaking down completely, but when the first tears trickle down her cheeks, she breaks into sobs. She lifts her clenched hands to her eyes and weeps. Nikolas goes over to her. He knows that he can do absolutely nothing, however much he wants to quench her sorrow. He bends over her, as if wanting to speak the words of consolation that she needs, but before he can say anything, she bursts out:

How can anyone endure to live here?

Nikolas strokes her hair and goes to the window, from which he sees:

THE COURTYARD

The coachman is putting on his cloak; he sits up and drives the carriage out.

THE DRAWING ROOM

Gisèle jumps up at the sound of the carriage. In her anxious and overwrought condition, she endows every sound with meaning. She goes to the window, looks out, and asks:

Where is he going?

To fetch the police! answers NIKOLAS.

The sound of the carriage dies away, but Gisèle remains standing with her face pressed against the windowpane. Nikolas goes to a lamp, by the light of which he takes out the sealed parcel that the stranger gave him in the inn, breaks the seal, and finds a book. Nikolas tiptoes over to a chair, lifts it carefully, turns it toward the lamplight, and sits down without a sound. Sitting there, he begins to read the book from the beginning.

LEIPZIG

GOTTLIEB FAUST ERBEN

MDCCLXX

A CURIOUS HISTORY OF VAMPIRES

BY PAUL BONNAT

The belief in vampires has ancient origins. These fearsome monsters, who cannot feel pity and are avid for the blood of young beings, whom they prefer beautiful and weak, are on the one hand . . . betrayed unfortunates who died with vengeance in their hearts, on the other, particularly odious criminals who return to torment innocent humans. Their passage only ever leaves scenes of bloodletting and death. Their power is diabolical. Men cannot . . .

LÉONE'S ROOM

Léone is lying in bed. The nurse is sitting in the room with her sewing things. Suddenly she raises her eyes. A number of little furrows have appeared on Léone's forehead. Her breathing becomes irregular and labored. Her face is twisted, as if she is tormented by fear and uncertainty. She opens her eyes, and her gaze is fixed and distant, as if held by someone a long way away. She looks like a medium under hypnosis. She is visibly no longer master of her own will, or she is under the influence of a power stronger than herself. In spite of her weakened condition, she raises herself on her elbow and shouts very loudly:

Yes . . . yes! as if someone has called to her.

The nurse has put aside her sewing things and is throwing off the blanket in which she has wrapped herself for the night. Outside the dog howls—penetrating, long, drawn-out howls. Léone raises herself still farther, until she is sitting on the edge of the bed.

LÉONE: Yes . . . I'm coming!

The nurse hurries over to her, but Léone, who moves just like somebody hypnotized, is on her way to the door. The nurse blocks her path by pushing a chair in front of her. The nurse stands before her and stares hard at her to catch her eye. The chair prevents Léone from advancing. The nurse tries gently to wake her, as one talks to a child crying in its sleep.

NURSE: You're dreaming . . . you're dreaming!

Now a remarkable change comes over Léone. Her tense expression relaxes; the hypnotic suggestion gradually seems to lose its hold on her, as if the other party has suddenly reconsidered and decided to wait for a better opportunity. She returns to her normal state of mind. She looks in surprise at the nurse, who leads her gently back to bed. Léone offers no resistance and even cooperates actively in getting into bed. The nurse sits down beside her.

NURSE: What were you dreaming about?

LÉONE: A voice . . .

NURSE: That spoke to you?

LÉONE: That called . . . commanded . . .

NURSE: What did it say?

Léone makes no reply.

Her eyelids close again. To all appearances she is sleeping the deep, sound sleep of an overtired child. The nurse watches her anxiously. This peaceful and apparently quite normal sleep inspires her with fear rather than confidence. She goes into the adjoining room to rinse some medicine bottles and the like. At almost the same moment, Léone wakes up with a start. She listens intently for the previous distant call; without a word she hurriedly throws off the blanket and steals out—so quietly that the nurse suspects nothing.

THE DRAWING ROOM

Gisèle at the window with her forehead pressed against the cold pane. Nikolas is sitting reading the book:

Nothing can destroy the supernatural actions of these horrible creatures that rise out of their tombs at night to suck the blood of the living during their sleep.

They drain them until they die. The only visible mark of their crime is a little red wound on the throat, the trace of the cruel teeth that opened the veins.

Like the reptile that fascinates the fragile bird that will become its prey, vampires exercise a mysterious charm over their victims. Neither the most stringent care, the most tender concern, nor the most fervent prayers . . .

Gisèle suddenly raises her head and looks out at the grounds. She cries out:

> Léone! . . .

Nikolas looks up.

> GISÈLE: Look! . . . Look! . . .
> There, on the grounds!

Nikolas hurries over to the window. The next moment they rush out into the hall; here they are joined by the manservant and the nurse, who come down the stairs in great agitation. Nikolas exclaims:

> Take the lantern!

He points to the lantern that the coachman has left at the foot of the stairs. The manservant's wife, the old housekeeper, comes in with her husband's jacket. He hastily puts it on. Then they all hurry out to:

THE GROUNDS

By the time they are out there, Léone is nowhere to be seen. They begin a thorough search of the grounds, which look ghostly with their moonlit sandstone statues. Some of the tree trunks are painted white. They look like skeletons, swaying backward and forward. Spiderwebs shine like silver. From time to time a bird flies off in alarm.

We begin by following the manservant, as he makes his way through bushes and undergrowth with the lantern held high over his head like a luminous hourglass. With his free hand he holds his jacket tightly round his neck. In the distance we hear Gisèle shouting anxiously:

Léone . . . Léone!

We see the old housekeeper standing on the stairs and looking out on the grounds. Gisèle's cries can still be heard. Now we follow Nikolas and Gisèle, who are together. Suddenly Nikolas stops and discreetly calls to Gisèle. He points out a group at some distance from them. On a stone table covered with ivy a white figure is lying prostrate. Bending over it a dark shape can be dimly discerned—as far as can be judged, that of an old woman. The white figure is lying in such a way that its head hangs over the edge of the table, and the attitude of the dark figure suggests that its lips must be in contact with the prostrate woman's throat. Nikolas and Gisèle, terror-stricken, make for the spot. Now the dark figure appears to notice them. Like a dog when it is disturbed while gnawing at its bone, the figure turns its head irritably and stares at the newcomers with the dead eyes of a blind person. With a grimace resembling nothing so much as a snarl, it bends down again over Léone, but straightens up once more as if abandoning its plan, and just as it looks as if it will turn away and go, it dissolves into thin air. Nikolas and Gisèle have reached the stone table. It is indeed Léone. Gisèle is already at her side. She looks in perplexity at Léone's thrown-back head. There is a gentle expression on Léone's lips, which are parted in a peaceful smile. Her hands are hanging down, white and limp. She looks in every respect as if she is dead. Nikolas puts his ear to her mouth to listen to her breathing . . . which is very weak . . . Gisèle cups Léone's face carefully in her hands and turns it toward her.

GISÈLE: Léone! Léone!

Léone slowly opens her eyes and looks for a long time in astonishment at Gisèle, who says in a disappointed, imploring voice:

But it's me . . . Gisèle!

Léone's eyelids close again. Only a narrow strip of white can be seen between the closed eyelids. Gisèle shows signs of wanting to call Léone back to consciousness.

NIKOLAS: Don't wake her!

At the same moment the manservant comes up, and Nikolas takes the lantern from his hand, letting the light fall on Léone's face.

GISÈLE: Look . . . blood! . . .

And she points at Léone's throat. The manservant opens his eyes wide and leans forward to look. Then he takes Léone in his arms, as if she were a child, and carries her to the castle. At the entrance the housekeeper is waiting. The nurse brings her a shawl or blanket; the housekeeper runs to meet the group and wraps Léone in the blanket. The little procession is now approaching the house. Nikolas runs on ahead to open the double door. The nurse goes up to the sickroom, shuts the windows, and arranges the bed. Meanwhile the manservant carries Léone up the stairs. Gisèle follows behind. Nikolas shuts the double door, goes into the drawing room, and continues his reading of the diary. His jaw is set in determination. The following page of the book is shown:

Nothing can deliver the miserable victims fated to suffer and die at the hand of vampires.

Woe to the young woman held in the grip of the monster. The physical and moral tortures that result are unspeakable. She can foresee her damnation, she cannot escape it, she struggles, she succumbs, she herself becomes a vampire, she chooses new victims from her immediate circle, who also succumb. It sometimes happens that an entire family, even an entire village, is devastated by this plague.

LÉONE'S ROOM

The manservant has laid Léone on the bed and now goes out. The nurse settles Léone and discovers the wound in her throat. She takes a wad of cotton wool, moistens it with a disinfectant rinse from a bottle, and dabs the liquid on the wound. Léone shudders, puts her hand on her throat, and groans. The nurse goes out.

GISÈLE (calling softly): Léone! . . . Léone! . . .

Léone wakes up but seems not to recognize Gisèle. She looks at her sister as if she has just woken from an evil and hideous dream. Then suddenly she seems to realize where she is. She shivers, puts her transparent hands to her face, and weeps silently.

GISÈLE (bending over her): Why are you crying?
No, no . . . Léone!

LÉONE (still weeping behind her white hands):
Yes, yes, yes . . . I am lost . . . I am sinking deeper
and deeper into the darkness . . . I am afraid . . .
I am afraid! . . .

Gisèle tries to comfort her by stroking her arm. Léone
takes her hands from her face. The nurse returns. Léone
glances round the room, as if looking for somebody.

LÉONE: Where is . . . ?

Gisèle hardly knows how to answer; she looks inquiringly
at the nurse, who answers:

The master . . . is asleep!

Léone smiles, gives a sigh of contentment, and closes
her eyes. She sighs again with relief and lies peacefully
for a moment with closed eyes. Then a remarkable
transformation occurs. A deathly pallor spreads across
her face. Her breathing becomes more rapid. Her mouth
opens. Her lips tighten. Then she opens her eyes. They
are now hard, almost malevolent. Her face takes on an

expression of lust when she sees Gisèle. The latter shrinks away uncomprehendingly, seized with fear and pain. The nurse gives her to understand that she had better go.

THE DRAWING ROOM

Nikolas is there with the old housekeeper, who with the thoughtfulness of an old woman has brought him a cup of strong coffee. Just as she is handing Nikolas the cup, Gisèle comes in. With a distracted expression she shuts the door mechanically and goes and sits down. The old housekeeper puts the other cup down beside Gisèle, who is completely absorbed by her recent strange experience. The other two look at her inquiringly.

> GISÈLE (back in the present): I think
> Léone is dying!

The old housekeeper goes. Gisèle shakes her head like somebody trying to get to the bottom of an insoluble mystery. Nikolas takes the cup and puts it in her hand. Mechanically she takes a gulp and puts the cup down; then she gives a sudden start, as if she has heard a piercing death scream. She sits for a moment with her mouth agape and her eyes wide open, as if she is still hearing it echo. Then she stands up, rushes to the window, and looks out. She seems surprised at not seeing anything and turns toward Nikolas.

GISÈLE: Didn't you hear something?

Nikolas shakes his head, goes up to her, and forces her to sit down in a chair; but she cannot refrain from turning toward the window.

NIKOLAS: You're tired!

He glances at her and turns back to his cup of coffee, which he put down a moment ago on a chair (or similar piece of furniture). Now he puts it very carefully on the table. An oppressive silence has settled over the house. Gisèle cries out:

Oh, this silence!

She presses her extended fingers against her breast, as if trying to free it from the pressure of the silence. Nikolas watches her for a little. Then he goes to the piano and begins to play. At the first touch she rises, goes slowly across the room, and stands behind him. She stands there with her hands behind her back until the music finishes. Then she says very quietly:

Thank you!

A moment later she adds:

I'll try to get a little sleep!

She takes a few steps, turns, and says:

You're not leaving us, I hope?

Nikolas rises and goes close up to her. She looks into his eyes like a trusting child. He gazes at her with infinite tenderness. Then he bends down and kisses her impulsively on the forehead. She gives him a smile of gratitude and goes into the adjoining room, where she lies down on the sofa and draws up a blanket over her. Nikolas stands gazing after her. A tear trickles from the corner of his eye down his cheek. From the other room he hears her voice:

Play something more!

He turns back to the piano and plays the same tune again. *The shrill sound of the old piano's loose keys resonates through the quiet rooms.* Gisèle's eyelids close. She sleeps.

As the last notes die away, the old manservant enters

the drawing room. Nikolas hastily turns toward him and puts his finger to his lips as a warning not to make any noise. The manservant says quietly:

The police are here.

Outside can be heard faintly the noise of a carriage rumbling over the cobbles in the courtyard. Nikolas leaves the room together with the manservant.

THE COURTYARD

The two men emerge from the house and stand at the head of the steps. The carriage drives up the last few yards. The horse walks in a curious manner, as if sunk in its own thoughts; then it stops abruptly. Joseph takes the lantern, which has been left on the steps, and slowly approaches the carriage. After a few paces he stops. Now he can see the whole carriage clearly—but the coachman is alone.

JOSEPH: Are you alone?

No answer! He takes a few more steps and repeats his question:

Are you alone?

Still no answer. Joseph turns to Nikolas, who in the meantime has come nearer. They look more closely at the coachman, who is sitting in a curious position, with his legs stretched out stiffly against the dashboard of the carriage. He has the reins in his hand, but they are hanging loose and lying on the ground. Joseph goes still nearer to the carriage and lifts the lantern. The coachman is sitting as if asleep. Nikolas clambers up behind the coachman's seat. Joseph hands him the lantern, which he holds in front of the coachman's face. He sees two staring, glassy eyes. Half paralyzed with terror, Nikolas hands the lantern back to Joseph. In the hope that the coachman is merely asleep, Nikolas puts his hand on his shoulder to waken him. But at the first touch the coachman's head sinks to his breast, and the whole body slumps forward.

Meanwhile the manservant has placed the lantern on the ground, and as soon as Nikolas has gotten down from the carriage, the manservant draws his attention to blood dripping from the floor of the carriage—drip, drip!

Both men stand for a moment as if hypnotized by this fearful new discovery. Then Nikolas hurries into the house. During all this, the other servants have gathered round the carriage. They shudder at the sight of the dead coachman and stare at the horse, which—with a corpse at the reins—has found its way home unaided. Joseph gets up onto the carriage . . .

THE DRAWING ROOM

Enter Nikolas. He shuts the door very quietly behind him, as if afraid that by making the slightest noise he will bring about still worse misfortunes. He tiptoes to the piano and extinguishes the two lights on it. As he is doing this, he cocks an ear to listen for Gisèle's breathing; then he resumes his reading of the diary:

The darkness makes them invulnerable. The vampires' satanic charm casts a spell on living men who can help with their fatal designs. It is said that in Hungary, one of them brought the village doctor into his service. With his soul sold to the devil, this doctor became the vile accomplice to the most atrocious crimes.

A vampire always succeeds in making the most dangerous man his ally.

As he reads, we hear in the distance the sound of horses' hooves on the paving stones . . . also the sound of the carriage being put away. Then silence reigns again around the old house. Nikolas listens out into the silence. Is he awake, or are all these fearful happenings merely a long, horrible nightmare? The heart of the old clock stops beating. After a moment, a deep sigh is heard from the corner of the room. Nikolas looks in that direction. A cello is standing there. One of the strings has slipped, and as he looks at it, another string breaks. Then silence again wraps its mantle around the room.

Nikolas begins reading again, but now the hideous, piercing screech of the doorbell is heard throughout the house. Nikolas puts down his book, goes to the window, and looks out. There he sees a man with his back turned to him. Joseph comes running from the stable buildings. Nikolas gathers that the stranger must be the doctor, for he and Joseph start discussing Léone's condition.

DOCTOR: How is she?

Joseph explains to him that things are going rather badly. The young lady has been found on the grounds. In answer to the doctor's exclamation of surprise, Joseph explains that she has climbed out of a window.

DOCTOR: Was she alone, then?

JOSEPH: Yes, just for a moment.

Nikolas catches only parts of the conversation. But while he watches the two men, something strange draws his attention. He can clearly distinguish the manservant's shadow in the moonlight, but he cannot see the shadow of the doctor or of the dog accompanying him. He stares

at the place on the ground where the shadows should be;
then the doctor's and the dog's shadows reappear next to
the manservant's, and Nikolas has the impression that he
recognizes both the doctor's and the dog's shadows from
the game at the beginning of the film.

Meanwhile the doctor has come in, followed by the
manservant, who is carrying his bag for him. When the
doctor enters the anteroom, Nikolas opens the door.
The stranger, who has hung up his hat, turns round. It is
Marc, whom Nikolas met in the little house behind the
factory. They look hard at each other for a moment.

NIKOLAS: Good evening!

Sir! answers the DOCTOR.

And it is he who eases the tension of the situation by
saying to the manservant:

Let's hurry . . . it's high time . . .

The doctor hurries to get in front of the manservant.
As soon as his back is turned, Nikolas goes up to the
manservant, takes the doctor's bag from him, and makes
him understand that he is to go in to Gisèle. The
manservant goes into the drawing room. Nikolas runs up

the stairs behind the doctor.

THE SICKROOM

The doctor hurries in and goes straight to the bed. The nurse's face takes on an expression of fear. She is giving the patient camphor. Léone is paler than before. Her features are hard and sharp, her lips blue. It is painful to see her and hear her breathing. She breathes slowly, gasping for air. Beside herself, the nurse turns to the doctor and says:

> It's going very badly!

> DOCTOR (curtly): Her pulse?

> NURSE: Very weak!

The doctor lifts one of the patient's eyelids, then examines her lips and gums. Next he takes Léone's wrist to feel her pulse. As he does so, he glances toward the door, where Nikolas is standing. An expression of surprise passes across the doctor's face; then he smiles the most fleeting of smiles. He lets go of Léone's hand and looks closely at her face. The nurse, who has been following his slightest movement, asks anxiously:

Is she dying?

DOCTOR (seriously): Yes.

He takes a few steps away from the bed and seems to fall into deep thought; then he says, as if talking to himself:

Perhaps we could save her . . .

Nikolas and the nurse follow him with their eyes. He speaks as if adding a link to the chain of thought he is forging for himself. Suddenly the doctor asks:

Will you give her blood?

The question takes Nikolas by surprise. He looks across at Léone. He feels certain the doctor is right, and if he does not immediately declare himself willing, it is because his feelings are divided between the obvious need to save Léone and his fear and uncertainty about this man. He looks at the nurse. Her anxiety has disappeared, and a gleam of confidence and hope shines in her eyes.

The doctor comes a step nearer and says, emphasizing each word:

[Immediately . . . this very moment!]

Nikolas makes no reply. He almost fails to notice the nurse, whose face reflects disappointment and sorrow. The doctor looks at him for a moment, then turns away and shrugs his shoulders.

Nikolas straightens up, takes off his coat, and rolls up one of his shirtsleeves. The nurse gets up with a happy smile and crosses to the table on which are bottles and instruments. The doctor, however, closes the door behind Nikolas, who has the feeling that he has let himself be caught in a trap.

THE DRAWING ROOM

Joseph goes to the door of the room where Gisèle is. His face shows surprise when he discovers Gisèle on the sofa; she is sitting motionless, with her legs drawn up under her and her head leaning back against the wall, staring fixedly at him with wide-open, startled eyes. As if talking to herself, she says:

Why does the doctor always come at night?

The manservant goes up to her in order to calm her.

THE SICKROOM

By the time we return, all the preparations for the blood transfusion have been completed. *The details of*

*the transfusion can be provided only after consulting
a specialist.*

THE DRAWING ROOM

Joseph returns from the room where Gisèle is. He has
evidently succeeded in calming her. He goes and sits in
the chair where Nikolas sat. He rests his head in his hand.
His gaze falls on the open diary. He reads what follows:

*This ally is often the person normally called first
to help the dying victim, the one who would have been
the vampire's most dangerous enemy without this pact.*

*The unfortunates slowly killed by the vampires
are haunted by the idea of suicide, for suicide
surrenders them to the demon. Any hope of salvation
is therefore lost.*

*For them the gates of heaven are forever closed,
all hope is lost.*

THE SICKROOM

The blood transfusion is now in progress. The only words
are curt orders like: Now!—Quickly!—That's enough!—Give
it to me!—Sit still! etc.

THE DRAWING ROOM

Joseph is reading the diary, which arouses his interest

more and more. It is as if he finds a connection between
what he reads and the fearful events that have taken
place around him. An extract from the diary is shown:

*The problems of life and death. For centuries the
existence of vampires has been related in strange
documents found in the libraries of the most famous
universities and convents. No one has the right to deny
the existence of vampires, even in our day and age.*

THE SICKROOM

The blood transfusion continues. Marc has positioned
himself outside the circle of light from the lamp, so that
he can see Nikolas in bright light while he himself sits
in the dark. Nikolas watches Léone's face anxiously and
closely during her struggle with death. Life slowly seems to
return to her, and her breathing becomes more peaceful.
She opens her eyes and looks at the people round her, but
she is much too enfeebled to speak and closes her eyes
again. Marc keeps a close watch on Nikolas, who grows
paler and paler. His eyes swivel slowly from Nikolas to
the patient and back to Nikolas again.

THE DRAWING ROOM

Another fragment of the diary is shown:

. . . The abominable misdeeds of these terrible ghosts are truly terrifying. One also finds a description of the only infallible method of making them disappear: The village of Kisilova was plunged into desperation by the sinister actions of an old woman who had been buried for nearly two centuries. One day, at dawn, her tomb was opened: she was found stretched out; her appearance was that of a person sleeping and enjoying very good health. A man took an iron stake and drove it into her chest, piercing her heart. Then she was truly dead, and the curse that hung over her and her victims died with her. From that moment, this area was delivered from the . . .

. . . waiting for deliverance by divine intervention. Twenty-two years ago, in this very country, a mysterious evil descended on the village of Courtempierre.

In a single week, there were eleven victims. The sign they all bore (a small bite mark on the throat) set off a search for the vampire responsible. The old people of the village remembered a rich and cruel woman who was so diabolical and suspect that upon dying she was refused the last rites. Her name was Marguerite Chopin and she was buried in the Courtempierre cemetery. They decided to open her tomb. But the one who was charged with piercing her heart was found lifeless near the coffin; he had not accomplished his task.

The mysterious crimes having stopped, the villagers soon forgot this . . .

THE SICKROOM

The blood transfusion is completed. While Marc himself is looking after the patient, the nurse leads Nikolas into an adjoining room, where she makes him sit down and prepares his bandage. The doctor stands bending over Léone.

[DOCTOR: Is he in a bad way?

NURSE (as she bandages Nikolas): Yes, rather.

DOCTOR: Come get this tablet!]

The nurse goes to get the tablet and gives it to Nikolas with a glass of water. He puts the glass down on a table near him. Then she covers him up, puts out the lamp, and goes into the sickroom, the door of which is ajar, leaving a strip of light visible. Meanwhile the nurse has been moving about, putting Léone's room straight. The doctor looks at her for a moment, then he says:

You can lie down now and sleep. I'll keep watch!

The nurse continues working with great zeal. The doctor now says to her in a cutting, almost hissing, tone:

Did you hear what I said?

The nurse looks at him in astonishment and encounters a cold stare. She realizes that there is no use in protesting; it would be in vain. She puts aside what she has in her hands and goes off. The doctor closes the door after her and looks around the room.

In the adjoining room Nikolas has dozed off. He feels very weak. In this weakened condition, he feels as if he is fainting, which is curious, because at one and the same time he is both fully conscious and far away. Suddenly he wakes from his doze and stares, openmouthed, at his bandaged arm. The blood can be seen seeping through the bandage. The wound is throbbing.

NIKOLAS: Doctor, doctor!

From the next room can be heard the doctor's cold, biting voice:

What is it?

NIKOLAS: The wound is bleeding!

DOCTOR: Go to sleep!

Nikolas lets his arm fall into the same position as before, dangling over the arm of the chair. In his semiconscious state he hears the doctor's voice, which has taken on quite a different tone; he whispers seductively and reassuringly, as if trying to convince a child and overcome its resistance by means of gentleness—or as one talks to somebody one wants to hypnotize. In his drowsy condition Nikolas hears only a few isolated words of this monologue, which in its entirety sounds something like this:

> You are suffering . . . you are tired . . . come with me . . . we shall become one . . . body, soul, blood . . . there is only one way of escaping from your suffering and finding peace . . . follow me . . . you will not be freed until you have taken your own life . . . come . . . I am waiting for you . . .

Then everything is quiet. In the silence Nikolas hears a sound: drip, drip! He leans forward and looks down. On the floor he sees the lantern that Joseph was carrying when the coachman arrived, apparently dead. The sound of dripping comes from somewhere near the lantern . . .

and now he sees what it is: blood running from his wound down onto his fingers and thence to the floor, where a regular pool has already formed. With an expression of bewilderment, he looks toward the door into the sickroom and calls:

Doctor! . . .

Again the doctor answers in an ice-cold, hissing voice:

What is it now?

NIKOLAS (desperately): I'm losing my blood!

DOCTOR: You're losing your blood?

NIKOLAS (urgently): Yes!

DOCTOR (slowly and emphatically): Nonsense! . . . It's here! . . . Your blood . . .

Nikolas sits there for a moment—uncomprehending and irresolute—then he leans forward and looks down. The sound of dripping has ceased, the pool of blood and the lantern have disappeared. When he lifts his hand, he sees that it is completely white and that the bandage is in

order. With a weary smile he settles himself comfortably
in the easy chair. He both sees and does not see the
light behind the door of the sickroom moving away and
disappearing.

THE DRAWING ROOM

Here the old manservant is sitting, completely absorbed in
the diary. Suddenly he raises his head, as if he has heard
a sound. He starts to his feet, with an overwhelming sense
of dread and foreboding. He is filled with a presentiment
of some horror or other. He goes to the window and
sees on the paving stones the shadow of a window on
the first floor. There is a light behind the window, and
the light is moving. He goes cautiously into the hall.
When he has climbed a few steps of the staircase, he
can see Marc in the window. In his hand he is holding
a lamp that he moves backward and forward several
times. The manservant stands there motionless and with
bated breath . . .

NIKOLAS

A remarkable change is taking place in Nikolas. His lips
open. His breathing becomes more rapid. He is apparently
in the throes of a sort of paroxysm, as if some stranger's
will is trying to gain control over him. *He slowly turns his
head and there—in the beam of moonlight—he is witness*

to a strange spectacle. There, in the very light from the moon, it is as if clouds of vapor are forming, swaying back and forth in a continuous movement. Nikolas shudders. The vapors take new shapes. Nikolas follows this strange spectacle with acute attention—he is increasingly absorbed by what he sees. It is as if the beams of moonlight are taking shape, becoming bodies. They slowly come to resemble the shape of a human being. Yet initially we can describe what Nikolas glimpses only as the shadowy outlines of a shape. But little by little the details become more precise, and now he sees the whole shape. Judging by its clothing, it must be an old woman—one who looks a great deal like the old blind woman he saw in the factory earlier that same night. But this creature is not made of flesh and blood. Through its dress we can distinguish (in the moonlight) the black shadow of a skeleton, and in place of a head, a sniggering skull. This entire action is accompanied by a sound that resembles the wind when it howls through the open windows and doors of an abandoned house, a sound that begins weakly and builds in intensity as the creature materializes.

Now the creature begins to move. Nikolas is riveted. He is overcome with horror. It stops next to him and stares at him with its empty eye sockets. Involuntarily, Nikolas has recoiled in his chair. Now the shape leans over him. The skull comes closer and closer. He thinks it's searching for his mouth, but it leans even lower and seems to want to stop at his throat. It stops there. He feels the soft touch of the skull's mouth brushing against the sensitive skin of his throat. During everything that has just happened, the look of horror has slowly disappeared from his face. He now closes his eyes in ecstasy. During this entire scene, we can hear the storm roaring both loud and soft, but when the skull reaches his throat, the storm seems to reach its peak and carries the feeling of horror to a climax. Then it slows down a little. He sees the shape slowly disappear. Then the shape fades into the moonlight, but it changes into a shadow before it disappears completely. Now Nikolas wakes with a start, filled with terror, depression, anxiety, and despondency. He looks up. The manservant is standing at his side with the glass of water that the nurse brought for him earlier, when he was on the point of fainting. At the same moment he realizes what has happened: it was his own blood that spoke to him in his dream, which is therefore nothing but a horrible mirror image of what has occurred at Léone's bedside. He pushes the glass of water away and makes his way past the manservant to the sickroom, which is almost completely dark, being lit only by a single small night-light. He tears the door open.

On entering, he sees Marc coming from the door leading out to the stairs. When he sees Nikolas, Marc's expression becomes hard and malevolent, and he increases his pace. Nikolas, however, reaches the bed first. He turns ice-cold with horror at the sight of Léone. She is lying there almost lifeless. She is whiter even than the bed linen covering her. Her face is heavy with sleep and relaxed, as if from the caress of a gentle hand. The little medicine bottle, which we recognize from the dream scene, is held in her hand, and with her last remaining strength we see she is trying to raise it to her mouth. At the very moment when the bottle touches her lips, Nikolas succeeds in snatching it from her. He throws it into a corner of the room, where it smashes. Then he hurries to Léone and uses his handkerchief to wipe a drop of poison from her lips.

Somewhere in the house a crash is heard, as if somebody has slammed the main door violently, then another crash, but less violent than before, as if somebody has loudly opened a door. The manservant seizes Nikolas involuntarily by the arm. Nikolas exclaims:

Stay here!

And he hurries out of the room. From the landing, he sees a light at the foot of the stairs. The light is whirling round. The shadow of the handrail flickers nervously on the wall. Nikolas is seized by a new fear: he is uneasy about Gisèle and hurries down. The nurse, who has been woken by the noise, darts into Léone's room as the manservant exits. Nikolas rushes through the drawing room into Gisèle's room. She is not there. He listens for her breathing, but not a sound reaches him. He lights a match. Her bed is empty. The blanket has been thrown back. He hurriedly searches the adjoining rooms, which are lying in darkness behind closed shutters, and returns to the hall.

From the moment he set off down the stairs, a penetrating, continuous howling has been audible outside. He goes to the door, under which at the same moment a white paper appears. He picks it up and reads the inscription: "Dust thou art, unto dust thou shalt return." He opens the door just quickly enough to see the shadow of the man with the wooden leg moving off the white paving stones of the courtyard and disappearing into the shadows of the trees. Nikolas hurries off in the same direction.

LÉONE'S ROOM

The nurse stands leaning over Léone. It is evident that the patient's strength is ebbing away. The nurse and the manservant are aware that everything will soon be over. Léone realizes it herself. She moans, sobs, and wails. The nurse consoles her as best she can. As for the manservant, he appears to be maturing in his mind some great project or other. Léone, who has great difficulty in getting the words out, says:

> I'm scared of dying . . . I am damned . . .
> Oh God, oh my God!

The manservant's mouth is twitching, which shows clearly that he is faced with an important decision. Now he gives a deep sigh, like someone who has finally come to a clear decision. Then he calls the nurse over to the door and says:

> She must not die now . . . You must keep her alive
> until morning comes . . . Do you hear me? . . .

The nurse nods. Then the manservant goes. On the threshold he stops.

JOSEPH: God help me!

He makes the sign of the cross and goes. The nurse returns to Léone's bed. She puts her hands up to her face, presses her fingers hard against her eyes, and sobs quietly.

THE WOOD
Nikolas is running in the direction of the factory.

THE CASTLE

The manservant comes pushing a wheelbarrow and stops in front of a toolshed, from which by the light of a lantern he takes a pickax, a spade, and a shovel; he puts these in the wheelbarrow. He is just about to go when he realizes that he has forgotten something. He goes back into the shed and takes both a long iron stake with a pointed tip and a wooden mallet. These objects likewise he puts in the wheelbarrow, fastens the lantern on the handle of the wheelbarrow, and sets off.

A FIELD

Nikolas enters at a run and suddenly falls headlong.

INSIDE THE CHURCHYARD

The manservant pushes his wheelbarrow along the wall. He makes for the churchyard gate.

A FIELD

Nikolas is lying on the spot where he fell. Suddenly his body divides in two. One part remains lying unconscious, while the other (Nikolas's ego) gets up with obvious difficulty. He slowly comes to and looks round in amazement. Not far off he notices an object on the ground. It is Gisèle's ring—the ring with the cross that her father gave her. He picks it up and examines it carefully, as if Gisèle has sent him a message by means of the ring; he looks round in the hope of finding a clue to which direction to go in order to find her again. Then he discovers some footsteps in the sandy earth, looking as if they have just been made before his very eyes by a pair of invisible feet—Gisèle's feet. He gets up and follows these footsteps. They lead him to:

THE BLIND WOMAN'S HOUSE

He goes in at the door, which opens easily, and finds himself in a dark yard at the back of the house. He gropes his way forward in the shadow of the house, until he finds a door without a handle. He opens this in turn. He now finds himself in the old laundry room, which he recognizes from his previous visit. From here he knows the way into the house and goes straight to the door at the other end of the laundry room. He enters the empty room adjoining it. Here everything is as he last saw it. His own footsteps are clearly visible in the dust on the floor; nobody has been here. He listens. Not a sound in the house.

He looks for the door into the room where the coffin stood before. It is locked. So something has happened since his last visit. He tries hard to open the door, but in vain. *He gives a start as a bat flying around the room in a panic violently collides with the window.*

He must and shall continue! From the landing, he discovers that the door into the consulting room is open. The moon throws a white beam on the stairs.

Is there someone in there? He steals along on tiptoe, holding on to the handrail, and reaches a point from which he can see most of the room. Inch by inch his view of the room increases, but there is nobody to be seen. On the other hand, a large box or something of the kind is standing in the middle of the floor. It is covered by a white cloth. *He enters the room. The door leading to the next room is open.* It was there that he saw the coffin before—and this must be the coffin, surely it must be the coffin under the white cloth. He goes up to it. The cloth is draped over somebody lying in the open coffin. The lid is leaning up against the wall. Merciful God! Gisèle! What has happened? Has he come too late? He looks again at the lid of the coffin standing by the wall. Something is painted on it in large capital letters. He reads: "Dust thou art, unto dust thou shalt return."

So these words were intended for her, not for him. He must make certain. He goes back to the coffin and carefully draws aside the cloth covering the corpse's face. But it is not Gisèle that he sees. It is his own face, rigid and open-eyed; his own head that rests wax-pale on the shavings in the black coffin. In bewilderment he bends over his own corpse. How can this be? What can it mean? Tentatively he puts out a hand in the direction of the dead face in order to make sure, but his courage fails and he pulls away his hand. He gets up and stands there motionless, paralyzed, petrified. Cold shivers run down his spine.

Then his horror-induced silence is interrupted by the sound of a key turning in a lock and a door opening and closing. This takes place in the corridor facing the door to the anteroom. Next we hear footsteps and the sound of a stick striking the ground at intervals. The sound at once disappears down to the cellar. He rushes to the landing. There is the door. It is a door with reinforced glass panes. The glass is murky and dusty, but sufficiently transparent for him to see that there is somebody in the room, somebody who has been dumped, hands tied together, on a large iron bed with no bedclothes. It is Gisèle! The door is locked, and he is just about to look for something with which to break it open when he hears somebody unlocking the main door. Through the murky little pane at the top of the door, he can see enough to ascertain that it is Marc coming. There is nothing for it but to return to the consulting room, and from here he sees Marc approaching the door between him and Gisèle; he is just putting the key in the lock when we again hear the footsteps of somebody with a wooden leg or stick. The footsteps come down the stairs. Marc abandons his plan and slips the key back in its hiding place, which is evidently unknown to the new arrival.

The man with the wooden leg comes limping down the stairs. Under his arm he is carrying a small toolbox. The two men meet and together make for the consulting room, from which Nikolas has followed everything through the half-open door. Now he is obliged to retreat farther. He has access only to the room where the coffin stood before.

Marc and the man with the wooden leg now stand beside the coffin. The man with the wooden leg searches for his screwdriver.

Nikolas has hidden behind the door of the next room, and as he stands there he discovers an open trapdoor leading down to the cellar. Standing right beside the trapdoor and peeping through the crack of the door, he is able to follow what the two men are up to.

Marc finds the stump of a cigar on the edge of his writing desk. He looks questioningly at the other: has he any matches? The other shakes the box to show that it is not empty. Marc lights the cigar.

The man with the wooden leg looks around. His screwdriver must be with the other tools in the room where Nikolas is. The man goes into this room and makes straight for the wall opposite the door. To avoid being seen as the man returns past him, Nikolas descends the ladder to the cellar, and when he is alone in the room again, he is able to stick his head up and see something of what is happening beside the coffin.

There the man is engaged in putting the lid on Nikolas's coffin. Marc stands there, enveloped in tobacco smoke, rocking backward and forward on his heels. He has stuck his thumbs in the armholes of his waistcoat, and his watchful, malevolent gaze flits rapidly across the coffin and the dead body.

The lid of the coffin has a square pane of glass just over the dead man's face.

From down in the coffin Nikolas sees the lid dropped into position over him. *He hears that someone is scraping, dragging, lifting, and dropping objects above him.* He hears the dull blows, first of a hand, then of a hammer, before the lid slips into the groove. He sees alternately something of Marc and of the man at work. Both of them peer down at him. Marc is in high spirits, whereas the other man's face reflects only the craftsman taking care that nothing goes wrong.

Now Nikolas hears, as he lies in the coffin, the lid being screwed down, hears the cutting and screeching noises of the screws as, one by one, they bore into the wood. It is impossible to imagine a death sentence having a more paralyzing effect than this sound. At intervals he sees through the glass the elbow of the man turning the screw. He hears the men's footsteps on the floor; then everything is quiet.

Now we hear the sound of the blind woman's footsteps and her stick. She is in the room, standing by the coffin. One hand holds a candle over the glass, the other lights it with a match, and now the sharp-boned blind woman's bony hand grasps the light. She bends her hideous face over the glass in the gleam of the candle. Her blind eyes are unable to see the dead man, but he can see her: she is taking her last leave of him. Her face disappears. Nikolas sees Marc moistening two fingers with his tongue and putting out the light. The blind woman's footsteps die away from the room, and now various men can be seen coming and stationing themselves on either side of the coffin.

The coffin is to be carried through the adjoining room, where at this moment Nikolas is hiding under the trapdoor. To clear the way, the man with the wooden leg goes over to the trapdoor. With his wooden leg he kicks away the wooden block holding the trapdoor open, and the trapdoor closes over Nikolas. The man gives the door a push so that it comes directly over the trapdoor, which in consequence cannot be opened.

Through the square of glass in his coffin Nikolas sees his surroundings change and realizes that he is being carried out. Ceilings, damp patches, door frames, cobwebs, and more door frames pass rhythmically through his field of vision. Then open sky and branches; he is being carried out of the house, far away . . .

Marc remains standing in the doorway. He throws away the butt of his cigar and searches in his pocket for his pipe, before going back into the room, from the window of which he takes a last look at the coffin.

THE FIELD

Nikolas is lying on the ground, as when we last saw him. He begins to return to consciousness. The dream he has just had enters his semiconsciousness. He opens his eyes a fraction, as if drowned in sleep, and sees the procession from his dream—at first making straight for him, but presently turning away. He turns to watch it and discovers that he is lying on the ground outside the churchyard. The funeral procession is making for the churchyard.

Suddenly he is awake—and the dream disappears; the strange procession literally vanishes into empty air. He asks himself whether the whole of this dream may not be a message from Gisèle, and if so what she is trying to tell him. He gets up and goes to:

THE ENTRANCE TO THE CHURCHYARD

There he sees the old manservant, who is pulling a coffin

out of the ground. The coffin is fully exposed, and the soil that covered it is piled around the grave, at the bottom of which lies the old, rotten coffin. The manservant now throws away his spade and uses his pickax to try and get the lid off. Nikolas has caught up with him. The two men exchange meaningful nods. Then Nikolas jumps down in the grave to help the manservant.

LÉONE'S ROOM

The dying Léone wakes up with a start. Her great eyes stare up at the ceiling, and her face expresses unspeakable and speechless astonishment. The nurse bends over her and asks:

What is it you can see?

Léone answers, almost ecstatically:

Death . . . Finally I'm no longer suffering!

THE CHURCHYARD

Nikolas and the manservant have succeeded in getting the lid off the coffin. They look with horror at the sight that meets their eyes.

In the coffin is lying the old blind woman. Her face is completely untouched, as if she were still alive. She is preternaturally pale and sallow. *Her eyes are open and vacant.* Neither her breathing nor her heartbeat can be heard. Nikolas looks at her by the light of the lantern. *Her face displays a horrifying expression of hatred and cruelty.*

LÉONE'S ROOM

Léone looks like somebody waiting and listening. The nurse again bends over her and asks:

[What do you hear?]

Léone grips the nurse's hand and answers:

[My father . . . is calling for me! . . .]

Her face still has the same expectant, startled expression.

THE CHURCHYARD

The manservant gives the iron stake to Nikolas and himself takes the mallet. Nikolas lifts the iron stake and directs the point under the blind woman's left breast. He raises and lowers the iron stake several times in order to take careful aim. Then he lifts it and, turning his face away, plunges it with all his strength into her heart. *The blind woman writhes in her coffin and lets out a terrible cry. Blood spurts around the point of the iron stake.* Nikolas signals to the manservant, who comes up and hammers the iron stake farther and farther in with the mallet. They both look very serious and full of energy. Blow after blow echoes around, *while the cries become weaker and eventually stop entirely.* As soon as the iron stake is hammered home, the two men break off from their work and take a step back. They stare down at the grave in disbelief. The blind woman's body has disappeared, *and in her place the coffin is now swarming with a multitude of spiders.*

LÉONE'S ROOM

Léone as before. The tension and suffering seem to have gone from her face. Staring straight ahead, she whispers as if in a trance:

[Now I feel strong . . . My soul is free!]

THE CHURCHYARD

The coffin full of spiders. The lid is pushed back into place on the coffin. In this shot we see only the coffin, the gravestone, and the manservant's hands at work. *Then the first shovelful of earth falls and resonates dully on the coffin.*

THE BLIND WOMAN'S HOUSE

The consulting room. There is a fire in the grate. Marc
is lighting another cigar. The man with the wooden leg
brings him a cup of coffee. Marc brushes some ash from
his trousers and takes a gulp of coffee. Suddenly he
raises his head and looks toward the window. The man
with the wooden leg observes his movements and goes
up to him. They both look at the window, where a face
now comes into view. It is Bernard, the man who was
murdered at the castle earlier in the night under such
mysterious circumstances. The face moves and looks in
anxiously, while Bernard's hands protect his eyes against
the moonlight. The two men in the room are seized with
terror. Marc bends forward and hastily puts out the light,
at the same time signaling to the man with the wooden
leg to put out the fire in the grate. The latter pours water
over the fire, which gives out a hissing cloud of steam.
Then Marc says:

[Go and see if the door is properly shut!]

The man with the wooden leg goes, leaving the door of
the room open, but it bangs behind him, as if blown by
a draught. Above the door is a large window. Marc recalls
the man with the wooden leg, as if regretting his order.
The man turns back hurriedly but finds the door closed.

In surprise he steps back a pace, and through the window above the door he sees a flickering light moving to and fro in the room. In his bewilderment he remains rooted to the spot. Then he hears a sound resembling that of a mother crooning a gentle lullaby over her child or of a doctor trying to reassure his patient during an operation. At the same time, one senses beneath the ingratiating and affectionate tone something threatening, hard, and almost ironic—a threat of revenge. Then we hear Marc's voice:

Oh! Oh! Oh!

The parrot's shadow. A moment of silence, suddenly shattered by the parrot's mocking, teasing laughter. The strangely soporific, monotonous voice now begins speaking again; then there is a piercing cry of terror, so frightful and horrifying that the man with the wooden leg rushes in utter panic to the door, tugs at it, hammers on it, and throws himself against it with all his strength. Meanwhile scream upon scream resounds, each more frenzied and hair-raising than the last.

Suddenly it is as if an invisible hand seizes the man with the wooden leg and hurls him against the wall opposite the door. The light over the door moves again. The door is opened violently. Marc comes out with every sign of consternation depicted in his face. A sudden gleam of light illumines the room. The parrot, terrified, takes flight. Marc hurries through the house, rushes out, and flees without pausing for a single moment.

But the man with the wooden leg lies motionless on the spot where he was thrown to the ground. His hands grip the handrail convulsively. His face is white, his look bewildered, and his lower jaw hangs down. His eyes are open and have a fixed, vacant expression, as if still seeing the fearful events of the previous day.

THE CHURCHYARD

The manservant has tidied up the grave and is now putting back the tombstone, on which can be read the following curious inscription: "Here lies Marguerite Chopin, born 4 February 1809, died 13 June 1867." Then a catalog of her virtues.

THE BLIND WOMAN'S HOUSE

We see Nikolas's hand inserting a key into the door guarding Gisèle. He finds it behind the piece of furniture where it is hidden and inserts it in the lock. The shot is taken in such a way that the spectator is uncertain whether the hand is real or not.

ROLLING COUNTRYSIDE

Marc is running at full speed, like a man pursued. He

keeps turning round, as if expecting to see his pursuer at every moment.

THE BLIND WOMAN'S HOUSE

Gisèle is lying on her bed, leaning against the wall, with her legs drawn up under her. Her hands are tied behind her back. Nikolas's hands appear on the screen, attempting to loosen her bonds. When the knot refuses to yield, he uses his teeth. Both the hands and Nikolas's profile are taken as in the previous shot, i.e., in such a way that the spectator is uncertain whether they are real or not.

ROLLING COUNTRYSIDE

Mist. Marc is running away like a man who has lost his reason. Where he is running there is no road or path.

LÉONE'S ROOM

Léone is at the point of death. She is quite calm. An angelic beauty suffuses her face. She smiles. Then she slowly closes her eyes. She gives a deep sigh, like a child just before it falls asleep. She has expired. A hand lays a little gold crucifix on her closed lips.

THE BOG

Marc has run right across the fields, still pursued by his invisible pursuer. Suddenly he is enveloped in mist. It is like steam rising from the earth. The mist gives everything a ghostly appearance. Marc is seized with terror. He does not know where he is. He can neither see nor hear. He is so confused and agitated that he does not know which way to take. He runs first in one direction, then in another, tries to retrace his steps, but is unable to see them because of the mist. He runs in a more and more random manner. He gets more and more lost. He stops for a moment. Then he sees, a short distance away, a light, which seems to come from a lantern, and the faint outlines of a gray shadow, which might be the shadow of a man. He calls, but instead of answering the shadow merely moves away from him. He decides to follow it. He runs in pursuit of it; but in spite of all his exertions, the distance between them remains the same. Speechless with terror, he pursues his frenzied course with his hands spread out in front of him, as if trying to scatter the mist. *He breathes with increasing difficulty; he gasps for breath. His expression becomes increasingly desperate. He stares straight ahead, as if he were trying to pierce through the mist. Darkness everywhere, mist everywhere. He feels he is surrounded by invisible, silent enemies. He splashes about. The bog water sprays around him. He is so out of breath he can barely draw air into his lungs. Suddenly he sinks to his knees. He stands abruptly. The coat loop of his jacket creeps on his neck. His limbs are deathly tired. He trips constantly. Now he comes to a stop. Up ahead, the shadow has also come to a halt. He calls to it again, but no answer, not a sound. He is overcome with terror. To his horror, he can feel himself sinking every time he stops. He feels he is caught in a trap. He calls to the shadow ahead of him in a fit of despair. It stops for a moment to listen. Marc regains hope, cries and calls again, but now the shadow turns away and quickly disappears. Bewildered, Marc looks at it, threatens it with his clenched fist, and begins to hurl insults at it. At the same moment, the light entirely disappears. Marc has already sunk into the mud to his knees. He struggles violently to avoid sinking deeper. He leans to one side, stands erect, leans to the other side, then repeats the same maneuver—without any success. On the contrary, he is only making it worse. He twists around in the mud, but when he finally succeeds in extricating one of his legs, he sinks even farther into the bog. He desperately fights this merciless enemy, made all the more terrifying by the fact that it is utterly silent. The invisible, elusive hand of the mud has him in its grasp. He digs like a madman, exhausted and gasping for breath as if he is about to die. Blood, mud, and sweat run into his eyes. He wipes his forehead with his sleeve. Suddenly he stops. He has exhausted his strength. He pushes his back against the mud. And he seeks to collect his thoughts. He cries out, then is silent for a moment. He cries out again, but no one responds to his call. Then suddenly it seems as if the mud is giving way below him. A deathly silence. His fate is inexorable. He will slip inch by inch until he meets his death, until he suffocates in the mud and darkness of the peat bog. He sinks to his chest. Frozen with terror, he pulls his hand out, calls out, and cries. He throws himself forward and digs in the mud as if his hands were claws. The water and mud compress his chest. The mud surrounds him like a gluey mass of tar. Once again he raises his voice and calls for help, but his lips can release only a hoarse moan. Now he sinks even quicker. The water is up to his face; he closes his mouth and presses his lips together; it reaches his mouth; he lowers his head and moans. At the moment his head disappears into the mud, his face is red and flushed as if it were about to burst. His last expression is a malevolent grimace. He raises his hand above his head, and this hand resembling a claw, with fingers tight together, covered in mud and bulging veins, is soon the only witness to Marc's death. Then it too disappears.*

THE RIVER

Crosscutting with the scenes described above recording Marc's death in the peat bog are scenes showing Nikolas and Gisèle on their way down to the river. When they reach the bank, they find it veiled in a white mist so thick as almost to blot out the opposite bank. A boat is lying

right at their feet. They jump down in it, and Nikolas
seizes the oars and starts rowing. When he has taken a
few pulls out into the river, the mist grows thicker; but
he continues to row. Now they cannot even see the bank
they have just left. Gisèle stares anxiously around, and
Nikolas rests on the oars to get his bearings. But they
see that they are completely enveloped in mist. They are
somewhat uneasy and confused. Nikolas puts his hands
up to his mouth as a megaphone and calls:

Hullo!

No answer. Nikolas calls again, and Gisèle joins in:

Hullo!

Far away a man's voice can be heard answering:

Hullo!

Nikolas stands up and shouts:

We're completely lost!

After a short pause he adds:

Where are we?

The voice from the other bank:

Across from the ferryboat!

Thank you! All right!

He sits down again and begins to row. He rows in silence for a moment without getting any closer to the bank. Gisèle is kneeling in the bow, keeping a lookout. The mist is now so thick that Nikolas can distinguish her only as a dark shadow. She says:

Do you think it's that way?

He rests on the oars, and the boat drifts with the gentle current. An eddy catches it, and it starts spinning round and round. Nikolas shouts:

Hullo!

The reply comes from a completely different direction than what he had expected and is much farther away than the first time.

VOICE: Hullo!

Nikolas and Gisèle shout together *as the boat spins:*

Hullo!

VOICE: . . . This way!

GISÈLE: Where are you?

VOICE (very distinctly, a word at a time):
Wait . . . we . . . will . . . light . . . a . . . fire!

NIKOLAS: Good!

Nikolas stays where he is but backs water so as not to be carried farther away by the current. On the bank we see the ferryman, whom we recognize from the opening of the film; he is signaling to a number of small boys to collect straw and wood for a bonfire. Presently a strong flame shoots up, but the light from the fire, instead of piercing the blanket of mist, seems able only to make it shine like a white wall.

In the boat Nikolas and Gisèle keep their eyes fixed on the place where they think the bank must be. Nikolas shouts impatiently:

Hullo!

FERRYMAN: Can you see the fire?

GISÈLE: What did you say?

FERRYMAN: Can you see the fire?

GISÈLE: No!

The ferryman stands and ponders for a moment. Then he goes to the bonfire himself to throw a bit more straw on it, saying to the boys:

Sing, children!

The boys exchange slightly embarrassed glances; then one of them begins to sing, and the others join in. A number of women who have arrived on the scene also join in the singing. The verse that they sing is:

Hark, an angel bears its light
Through the gates of heaven.
By God's angel's beams so bright
All the black nocturnal shades are driven.

During the singing the boat has come close to the bank. *The ferryman passes before the fire.* For the two people in the boat the singing sounds curiously muffled, even if they can hear it distinctly. Then it ceases. The ferryman hears the oars on the water. Nikolas and Gisèle now see the fire and the ferryman, who is walking along the bank, following the rhythmic sound of the oars and the creaking of the oarlocks. *Gisèle alone. The oars.* Now the boat pulls into the bank, and the ferryman wades out into the water in order to catch hold of the prow and pull the boat ashore.

Nikolas and Gisèle jump ashore. When they reach the top of the bank, the mist melts away. The path leads them into a little cluster of birches. The sun breaks through the clouds. They have left the night and the shadows behind them. In front of them are mountain ranges and light. They still hear, as if proclaimed by heavenly bells:

Hark, an angel bears its light . . .

CARMILLA

BY SHERIDAN LE FANU

PROLOGUE

Upon a paper attached to the Narrative which follows, Doctor Hesselius has written a rather elaborate note, which he accompanies with a reference to his Essay on the strange subject which the MS illuminates.

This mysterious subject he treats, in that Essay, with his usual learning and acumen, and with remarkable directness and condensation. It will form but one volume of the series of that extraordinary man's collected papers.

As I publish the case, in these volumes, simply to interest the "laity," I shall forestall the intelligent lady, who relates it, in nothing; and, after due consideration, I have determined, therefore, to abstain from presenting any *précis* of the learned doctor's reasoning, or extract from his statement on a subject which he describes as "involving, not improbably, some of the profoundest arcana of our dual existence, and its intermediates."

I was anxious, on discovering this paper, to re-open the correspondence commenced by Doctor Hesselius, so many years before, with a person so clever and careful as his informant seems to have been. Much to my regret, however, I found that she had died in the interval.

She, probably, could have added little to the Narrative which she communicates in the following pages, with, so far as I can pronounce, such a conscientious particularity.

CHAPTER I
AN EARLY FRIGHT

In Styria, we, though by no means magnificent people, inhabit a castle, or schloss. A small income, in that part of the world, goes a great way. Eight or nine hundred a year does wonders. Scantily enough ours would have answered among wealthy people at home. My father is English, and I bear an English name, although I never saw England. But here, in this lonely and primitive place, where everything is so marvellously cheap, I really don't see how ever so much more money would at all materially add to our comforts, or even luxuries.

My father was in the Austrian service, and retired upon a pension and his patrimony, and purchased this feudal residence, and the small estate on which it stands, a bargain.

Nothing can be more picturesque or solitary. It stands on a slight eminence in a forest. The road, very old and narrow, passes in front of its drawbridge, never raised in my time, and its moat, stocked with perch, and sailed over by many swans, and floating on its surface white fleets of water-lilies.

Over all this the schloss shows its many-windowed front; its towers, and its Gothic chapel.

The forest opens in an irregular and very picturesque glade before its gate, and at the right a steep Gothic bridge carries the road over a stream that winds in deep shadow through the wood.

I have said that this is a very lonely place. Judge whether I say truth. Looking from the hall door towards the road, the forest in which our castle stands extends fifteen miles to the right, and twelve to the left. The nearest inhabited village is about seven of your English miles to the left. The nearest inhabited schloss of any historic associations is that of old General Spielsdorf, nearly twenty miles away to the right.

I have said "the nearest *inhabited* village," because there is, only three miles westward, that is to say in the direction of General Spielsdorf's schloss, a ruined village, with its quaint little church, now roofless, in the aisle of which are the mouldering tombs of the proud family of Karnstein, now extinct, who once owned the equally desolate château which, in the thick of the forest, overlooks the silent ruins of the town.

Respecting the cause of the desertion of this striking and melancholy spot, there is a legend which I shall relate to you another time.

I must tell you now, how very small is the party who constitute the inhabitants of our castle. I don't include servants, or those dependants who occupy rooms in the buildings attached to the schloss. Listen, and wonder! My father, who is the kindest man on earth, but growing old; and I, at the date of my story, only nineteen. Eight years have passed since then. I and my father constituted the family at the schloss. My mother, a Styrian lady, died in my infancy, but I had a good-natured governess, who had been with me from, I might almost say, my infancy. I could not remember the time when her fat, benignant face was not a familiar picture in my memory. This was Madame Perrodon, a native of Berne, whose care and good nature in part supplied to me the loss of my mother, whom I do not even remember, so early I lost her. She made a third at our little dinner party. There was a fourth, Mademoiselle De Lafontaine, a lady such as you term, I believe, a "finishing governess." She spoke French and German, Madame Perrodon French and broken English, to which my father and I added English, which, partly to prevent its becoming a lost language among us, and partly from patriotic motives, we spoke every day. The consequence was a Babel, at which strangers used to laugh, and which I shall make no attempt to reproduce in this narrative. And there were two or three young lady friends besides, pretty nearly of my own age, who were occasional visitors, for longer or shorter terms; and these visits I sometimes returned.

These were our regular social resources; but of course there were chance visits from "neighbours" of only five or six leagues distance. My life was, notwithstanding, rather a solitary one, I can assure you.

My gouvernantes had just so much control over me as you might conjecture such sage persons would have in the case of a rather spoiled girl, whose only parent allowed her pretty nearly her own way in everything.

The first occurrence in my existence, which produced a terrible impression upon my mind, which, in fact, never has been effaced, was one of the very earliest incidents of my life which I can recollect. Some people will think it so trifling that it should not be recorded here. You will see, however, by-and-by, why I mention it. The nursery, as it was called, though I had it all to myself, was a large room in the upper storey of the castle, with a steep oak roof. I can't have been more than six years old, when one night I awoke, and looking round the room from my bed, failed to see the nursery-maid. Neither was my nurse there; and I thought myself alone. I was not frightened, for I was one of those happy children who are studiously kept in ignorance of ghost stories, of fairy tales, and of all such lore as makes us cover up our heads when the door creaks suddenly, or the flicker of an expiring candle makes the shadow of a bed-post dance upon the wall, nearer to our faces. I was vexed and insulted at finding myself, as I conceived, neglected, and I began to whimper, preparatory to a hearty bout of roaring; when to my surprise, I saw a solemn, but very pretty face looking at me from the side of the bed. It was that of a young lady who was kneeling, with her hands under the coverlet. I looked at her with a kind of pleased wonder, and ceased whimpering. She caressed me with her hands, and lay down beside me on the bed, and drew me towards her, smiling; I felt immediately delightfully soothed, and fell asleep again. I was wakened by a sensation as if two needles ran into my breast very deep at the same moment, and I cried loudly. The lady started back, with her eyes fixed on me, and then slipped down upon the floor, and, as I thought, hid herself under the bed.

I was now for the first time frightened, and I yelled with all my might and main. Nurse, nursery-maid, housekeeper, all came running in, and hearing my story, they made light of it, soothing me all they could meanwhile. But, child as I was, I could perceive that their faces were pale with an unwonted look of anxiety, and I saw them look under the bed, and about the room, and peep under tables and pluck open cupboards; and the housekeeper whispered to the nurse: "Lay your hand along that hollow in the bed; some one *did* lie there, so sure as you did not; the place is still warm."

I remember the nursery-maid petting me, and all three examining my chest, where I told them I felt the puncture, and pronouncing that there was no sign visible that any such thing had happened to me.

The housekeeper and the two other servants who were in charge of the nursery remained sitting up all night; and from that time a servant always sat up in the nursery until I was about fourteen.

I was very nervous for a long time after this. A doctor was called in; he was pallid and elderly. How well I remember his long saturnine face, slightly pitted with small-pox, and his chestnut wig. For a good while, every second day, he came and gave me medicine, which of course I hated.

The morning after I saw this apparition I was in a state of terror, and could not bear to be left alone, daylight though it was, for a moment.

I remember my father coming up and standing at the bed-side, and talking cheerfully, and asking the nurse a number of questions, and laughing very heartily at one of the answers; and patting me on the shoulder, and kissing me, and telling me not to be frightened, that it was nothing but a dream and could not hurt me.

But I was not comforted, for I knew the visit of the strange woman was not a dream; and I was *awfully* frightened.

I was a little consoled by the nursery-maid's assuring me that it was she who had come and looked at me, and lain down beside me in the bed, and that I must have been half-dreaming not to have known her face. But this, though supported by the nurse, did not quite satisfy me.

I remember, in the course of that day, a venerable old man, in a black cassock, coming into the room with the nurse and housekeeper, and talking a little to them, and very kindly to me; his face was very sweet and gentle, and he told me they were going to pray, and joined my hands together, and desired me to say, softly, while they were praying, "Lord hear all good prayers for us, for Jesus' sake." I think these were the very words, for I often repeated them to myself, and my nurse used for years to make me say them in my prayers.

I remember so well the thoughtful sweet face of that white-haired old man, in his black cassock, as he stood in that rude, lofty, brown room, with the clumsy furniture of a fashion three hundred years old about him, and the scanty light entering its shadowy atmosphere through the small lattice. He kneeled, and the three women with him, and he prayed aloud with an earnest quavering voice for, what appeared to me, a long time. I forget all my life preceding that event, and for some time after it is all obscure also, but the scenes I have just described stand out vivid as the isolated pictures of the phantasmagoria surrounded by darkness.

CHAPTER II

A GUEST

I am now going to tell you something so strange that it will require all your faith in my veracity to believe my story. It is not only true, nevertheless, but truth of which I have been an eye-witness.

It was a sweet summer evening, and my father asked me, as he sometimes did, to take a little ramble with him along that beautiful forest vista which I have mentioned as lying in front of the schloss.

"General Spielsdorf cannot come to us so soon as I had hoped," said my father, as we pursued our walk.

He was to have paid us a visit of some weeks, and we had expected his arrival next day. He was to have brought with him a young lady, his niece and ward, Mademoiselle Rheinfeldt, whom I had never seen, but whom I had heard described as a very charming girl, and in whose society I had promised myself many happy days. I was more disappointed than a young lady living in a town or a bustling neighbourhood can possibly imagine. This visit, and the new acquaintance it promised, had furnished my day dream for many weeks.

"And how soon does he come?" I asked.

"Not till autumn. Not for two months, I dare say," he answered. "And I am very glad now, dear, that you never knew Mademoiselle Rheinfeldt."

"And why?" I asked, both mortified and curious.

"Because the poor young lady is dead," he replied. "I quite forgot I had not told you, but you were not in the room when I received the General's letter this evening."

I was very much shocked. General Spielsdorf had mentioned in his first letter, six or seven weeks before, that she was not so well as he would wish her, but there was nothing to suggest the remotest suspicion of danger.

"Here is the General's letter," he said, handing it to me. "I am afraid he is in great affliction; the letter appears to me to have been written very nearly in distraction."

We sat down on a rude bench, under a group of magnificent lime-trees. The sun was setting with all its melancholy splendour behind the sylvan horizon, and the stream that flows beside our home, and passes under the steep old bridge I have mentioned, wound through many a group of noble trees, almost at our feet, reflecting in its current the fading crimson of the sky. General Spielsdorf's letter was so extraordinary, so vehement, and in some places so self-contradictory, that I read it twice over—the second time aloud to my father—and was still unable to account for it, except by supposing that grief had unsettled his mind.

It said,

"I have lost my darling daughter, for as such I loved

her. During the last days of dear Bertha's illness I was
not able to write to you. Before then I had no idea of her
danger. I have lost her, and now learn *all*, too late. She
died in the peace of innocence, and in the glorious hope of
a blessed futurity. The fiend who betrayed our infatuated
hospitality has done it all. I thought I was receiving into
my house innocence, gaiety, a charming companion for
my lost Bertha. Heavens! what a fool I have been! I thank
God my child died without a suspicion of the cause of her
sufferings. She is gone without so much as conjecturing
the nature of her illness, and the accursed passion of the
agent of all this misery. I devote my remaining days to
tracking and extinguishing a monster. I am told I may
hope to accomplish my righteous and merciful purpose.
At present there is scarcely a gleam of light to guide me.
I curse my conceited incredulity, my despicable affectation
of superiority, my blindness, my obstinacy—all—too late. I
cannot write or talk collectedly now. I am distracted. So
soon as I shall have a little recovered, I mean to devote
myself for a time to inquiry, which may possibly lead me
as far as Vienna. Some time in the autumn, two months
hence, or earlier if I live, I will see you—that is, if you
permit me; I will then tell you all that I scarce dare put
upon paper now. Farewell. Pray for me, dear friend."

In these terms ended this strange letter. Though I
had never seen Bertha Rheinfeldt my eyes filled with

tears at the sudden intelligence; I was startled, as well as profoundly disappointed.

The sun had now set, and it was twilight by the time I had returned the General's letter to my father.

It was a soft clear evening, and we loitered, speculating upon the possible meanings of the violent and incoherent sentences which I had just been reading. We had nearly a mile to walk before reaching the road that passes the schloss in front, and by that time the moon was shining brilliantly. At the drawbridge we met Madame Perrodon and Mademoiselle De Lafontaine, who had come out, without their bonnets, to enjoy the exquisite moonlight.

We heard their voices gabbling in animated dialogue as we approached. We joined them at the drawbridge, and turned about to admire with them the beautiful scene.

The glade through which we had just walked lay before us. At our left the narrow road wound away under clumps of lordly trees, and was lost to sight amid the thickening forest. At the right the same road crosses the steep and picturesque bridge, near which stands a ruined tower which once guarded that pass; and beyond the bridge an abrupt eminence rises, covered with trees, and showing in the shadows some grey ivy-clustered rocks.

Over the sward and low grounds a thin film of mist was stealing, like smoke, marking the distances with a transparent veil; and here and there we could see the river faintly flashing in the moonlight.

No softer, sweeter scene could be imagined. The news I had just heard made it melancholy; but nothing could disturb its character of profound serenity, and the enchanted glory and vagueness of the prospect.

My father, who enjoyed the picturesque, and I stood looking in silence over the expanse beneath us. The two good governesses, standing a little way behind us, discoursed upon the scene, and were eloquent upon the moon.

Madame Perrodon was fat, middle-aged, and romantic, and talked and sighed poetically. Mademoiselle De Lafontaine—in right of her father, who was a German, assumed to be psychological, metaphysical, and something of a mystic—now declared that when the moon shone with a light so intense it was well known that it indicated a special spiritual activity. The effect of the full moon in such a state of brilliancy was manifold. It acted on dreams, it acted on lunacy, it acted on nervous people; it had marvellous physical influences connected with life. Mademoiselle related that her cousin, who was mate of a merchant ship, having taken a nap on deck on such a night, lying on his back, with his face full in the light of the moon, had wakened, after a dream of an old woman clawing him by the cheek, with his features horribly drawn to one side; and his countenance had never quite recovered its equilibrium.

"The moon, this night," she said, "is full of odylic and magnetic influence—and see, when you look behind you at the front of the schloss, how all its windows flash and twinkle with that silvery splendour, as if unseen hands had lighted up the rooms to receive fairy guests."

There are indolent states of the spirits in which, indisposed to talk ourselves, the talk of others is pleasant to our listless ears; and I gazed on, pleased with the tinkle of the ladies' conversation.

"I have got into one of my moping moods to-night," said my father, after a silence, and quoting Shakespeare, whom, by way of keeping up our English, he used to read aloud, he said:

> "In truth I know not why I am so sad:
> It wearies me; you say it wearies you;
> But how I got it—came by it.

"I forget the rest. But I feel as if some great misfortune were hanging over us. I suppose the poor General's afflicted letter has had something to do with it."

At this moment the unwonted sound of carriage wheels and many hoofs upon the road arrested our attention.

They seemed to be approaching from the high ground overlooking the bridge, and very soon the equipage emerged from that point. Two horsemen first crossed the bridge, then came a carriage drawn by four horses, and two men rode behind.

It seemed to be the travelling carriage of a person of rank; and we were all immediately absorbed in watching that very unusual spectacle. It became, in a few moments, greatly more interesting, for just as the carriage had passed the summit of the steep bridge, one of the leaders, taking fright, communicated his panic to the rest, and after a plunge or two, the whole team broke into a wild gallop together, and dashing between the horsemen who rode in front, came thundering along the road towards us with the speed of a hurricane.

The excitement of the scene was made more painful by the clear, long-drawn screams of a female voice from the carriage window.

We all advanced in curiosity and horror; my father in silence, the rest with various ejaculations of terror.

Our suspense did not last long. Just before you reach the castle drawbridge, on the route they were coming, there stands by the roadside a magnificent lime-tree, on the other side stands an ancient stone cross, at sight of which the horses, now going at a pace that was perfectly frightful, swerved so as to bring the wheel over the projecting roots of the tree.

I knew what was coming. I covered my eyes, unable to see it out, and turned my head away; at the same moment I heard a cry from my lady-friends, who had gone on a little.

Curiosity opened my eyes, and I saw a scene of utter confusion. Two of the horses were on the ground, the carriage lay upon its side with two wheels in the air; the men were busy removing the traces, and a lady, with a commanding air and figure, had got out, and stood with clasped hands, raising the handkerchief that was in them every now and then to her eyes. Through the carriage door was now lifted a young lady, who appeared to be lifeless. My dear old father was already beside the elder lady, with his hat in his hand, evidently tendering his aid and the resources of his schloss. The lady did not appear to hear him, or to have eyes for anything but the slender girl who was being placed against the slope of the bank.

I approached; the young lady was apparently stunned, but she was certainly not dead. My father, who piqued himself on being something of a physician, had just had his fingers to her wrist and assured the lady, who declared herself her mother, that her pulse, though faint and irregular, was undoubtedly still distinguishable. The lady clasped her hands and looked upward, as if in a momentary transport of gratitude; but immediately she broke out again in that theatrical way which is, I believe, natural to some people.

She was what is called a fine-looking woman for her
time of life, and must have been handsome; she was tall,
but not thin, and dressed in black velvet, and looked rather
pale, but with a proud and commanding countenance,
though now agitated strangely.

"Was ever being so born to calamity?" I heard her
say, with clasped hands, as I came up. "Here am I, on
a journey of life and death, in prosecuting which to lose
an hour is possibly to lose all. My child will not have
recovered sufficiently to resume her route for who can say
how long. I must leave her; I cannot, dare not, delay. How
far on, sir, can you tell, is the nearest village? I must leave
her there; and shall not see my darling, or even hear of
her till my return, three months hence."

I plucked my father by the coat, and whispered earnestly
in his ear: "Oh! papa, pray ask her to let her stay with
us—it would be so delightful. Do, pray."

"If Madame will entrust her child to the care of
my daughter, and of her good gouvernante, Madame
Perrodon, and permit her to remain as our guest, under
my charge, until her return, it will confer a distinction and
an obligation upon us, and we shall treat her with all the
care and devotion which so sacred a trust deserves."

"I cannot do that, sir, it would be to task your kindness
and chivalry too cruelly," said the lady, distractedly.

"It would, on the contrary, be to confer on us a very

great kindness at the moment when we most need it. My daughter has just been disappointed by a cruel misfortune, in a visit from which she had long anticipated a great deal of happiness. If you confide this young lady to our care it will be her best consolation. The nearest village on your route is distant, and affords no such inn as you could think of placing your daughter at; you cannot allow her to continue her journey for any considerable distance without danger. If, as you say, you cannot suspend your journey, you must part with her to-night, and nowhere could you do so with more honest assurances of care and tenderness than here."

There was something in this lady's air and appearance so distinguished, and even imposing, and in her manner so engaging, as to impress one, quite apart from the dignity of her equipage, with a conviction that she was a person of consequence.

By this time the carriage was replaced in its upright position, and the horses, quite tractable, in the traces again.

The lady threw on her daughter a glance which I fancied was not quite so affectionate as one might have anticipated from the beginning of the scene; then she beckoned slightly to my father, and withdrew two or three steps with him out of hearing; and talked to him with a fixed and stern countenance, not at all like that with which she had hitherto spoken.

I was filled with wonder that my father did not seem to perceive the change, and also unspeakably curious to learn what it could be that she was speaking, almost in his ear, with so much earnestness and rapidity.

Two or three minutes at most I think she remained thus employed, then she turned, and a few steps brought her to where her daughter lay, supported by Madame Perrodon. She kneeled beside her for a moment and whispered, as Madame supposed, a little benediction in her ear; then hastily kissing her she stepped into her carriage, the door was closed, the footmen in stately liveries jumped up behind, the outriders spurred on, the postillions cracked their whips, the horses plunged and broke suddenly into a furious canter that threatened soon again to become a gallop, and the carriage whirled away, followed at the same rapid pace by the two horsemen in the rear.

CHAPTER III

WE COMPARE NOTES

We followed the *cortège* with our eyes until it was swiftly lost to sight in the misty wood; and the very sound of the hoofs and the wheels died away in the silent night air.

Nothing remained to assure us that the adventure had

not been an illusion of a moment but the young lady, who just at that moment opened her eyes. I could not see, for her face was turned from me, but she raised her head, evidently looking about her, and I heard a very sweet voice ask complainingly, "Where is mamma?"

Our good Madame Perrodon answered tenderly, and added some comfortable assurances.

I then heard her ask:

"Where am I? What is this place?" and after that she said, "I don't see the carriage; and Matska, where is she?"

Madame answered all her questions in so far as she understood them; and gradually the young lady remembered how the misadventure came about, and was glad to hear that no one in, or in attendance on, the carriage was hurt; and on learning that her mamma had left her here, till her return in about three months, she wept.

I was going to add my consolations to those of Madame Perrodon when Mademoiselle De Lafontaine placed her hand upon my arm, saying:

"Don't approach, one at a time is as much as she can at present converse with; a very little excitement would possibly overpower her now."

As soon as she is comfortably in bed, I thought, I will run up to her room and see her.

My father in the meantime had sent a servant on horseback for the physician, who lived about two leagues away; and a bed-room was being prepared for the young lady's reception.

The stranger now rose, and leaning on Madame's arm, walked slowly over the drawbridge and into the castle gate.

In the hall, servants waited to receive her, and she was conducted forthwith to her room.

The room we usually sat in as our drawing-room is long, having four windows, that looked over the moat and drawbridge, upon the forest scene I have just described.

It is furnished in old carved oak, with large carved cabinets, and the chairs are cushioned with crimson Utrecht velvet. The walls are covered with tapestry, and surrounded with great gold frames, the figures being as large as life, in ancient and very curious costume, and the subjects represented are hunting, hawking, and generally festive. It is not too stately to be extremely comfortable; and here we had our tea, for with his usual patriotic leanings my father insisted that the national beverage should make its appearance regularly with our coffee and chocolate.

We sat there this night, and with candles lighted, were talking over the adventure of the evening.

Madame Perrodon and Mademoiselle De Lafontaine were both of our party. The young stranger had hardly lain down in her bed when she sank into a deep sleep; and those ladies had left her in the care of a servant.

"How do you like our guest?" I asked, as soon as Madame entered. "Tell me all about her."

"I like her extremely," answered Madame, "she is, I almost think, the prettiest creature I ever saw; about your age, and so gentle and nice."

"She is absolutely beautiful," threw in Mademoiselle, who had peeped for a moment into the stranger's room.

"And such a sweet voice!" added Madame Perrodon.

"Did you remark a woman in the carriage, after it was set up again, who did not get out," inquired Mademoiselle, "but only looked from the window?"

"No, we had not seen her."

Then she described a hideous black woman, with a sort of coloured turban on her head, who was gazing all the time from the carriage window, nodding and grinning derisively towards the ladies, with gleaming eyes and large white eye-balls, and her teeth set as if in fury.

"Did you remark what an ill-looking pack of men the servants were?" asked Madame.

"Yes," said my father, who had just come in, "ugly, hang-dog looking fellows, as ever I beheld in my life. I hope they mayn't rob the poor lady in the forest. They are clever rogues, however; they got everything to rights in a minute."

"I dare say they are worn out with too long travelling," said Madame. "Besides looking wicked, their faces were so strangely lean, and dark, and sullen. I am very curious, I own; but I dare say the young lady will tell us all about it to-morrow, if she is sufficiently recovered."

"I don't think she will," said my father, with a mysterious smile, and a little nod of his head, as if he knew more about it than he cared to tell us.

This made me all the more inquisitive as to what had passed between him and the lady in the black velvet, in the brief but earnest interview that had immediately preceded her departure.

We were scarcely alone, when I entreated him to tell me. He did not need much pressing.

"There is no particular reason why I should not tell you. She expressed a reluctance to trouble us with the care of her daughter, saying she was in delicate health, and nervous, but not subject to any kind of seizure—she volunteered that—nor to any illusion; being, in fact, perfectly sane."

"How very odd to say all that!" I interpolated. "It was so unnecessary."

"At all events it *was* said," he laughed, "and as you wish to know all that passed, which was indeed very little, I tell you. She then said, 'I am making a long journey of *vital* importance'—she emphasized the word—'rapid and secret; I shall return for my child in three months; in the meantime, she will be silent as to who we are, whence we come, and whither we are travelling.' That is all she said. She spoke very pure French. When she said the word 'secret,' she paused for a few seconds, looking sternly, her eyes fixed on mine. I fancy she makes a great point of that. You saw how quickly she was gone. I hope I have not done a very foolish thing, in taking charge of the young lady."

For my part, I was delighted. I was longing to see and talk to her; and only waiting till the doctor should give me leave. You, who live in towns, can have no idea how great an event the introduction of a new friend is, in such a solitude as surrounded us.

The doctor did not arrive until nearly one o'clock; but I could no more have gone to my bed and slept, than I could have overtaken, on foot, the carriage in which the princess in black velvet had driven away.

When the physician came down to the drawing-room, it was to report very favourably upon his patient. She was now sitting up, her pulse quite regular, apparently perfectly well. She had sustained no injury, and the little shock to her nerves had passed away quite harmlessly. There could be no harm certainly in my seeing her, if we both wished it; and, with this permission, I sent, forthwith, to know whether she would allow me to visit her for a few minutes in her room.

The servant returned immediately to say that she desired nothing more.

You may be sure I was not long in availing myself of this permission.

Our visitor lay in one of the handsomest rooms in the schloss. It was, perhaps, a little stately. There was a somber piece of tapestry opposite the foot of the bed, representing Cleopatra with the asp to her bosom; and other solemn classic scenes were displayed, a little faded, upon the other walls. But there was gold carving, and rich and varied colour enough in the other decorations of the room, to more than redeem the gloom of the old tapestry.

There were candles at the bed-side. She was sitting up; her slender pretty figure enveloped in the soft silk dressing-gown, embroidered with flowers, and lined with thick quilted silk, which her mother had thrown over her feet as she lay upon the ground.

What was it that, as I reached the bed-side and had just begun my little greeting, struck me dumb in a moment, and made me recoil a step or two before her? I will tell you.

I saw the very face which had visited me in my childhood at night, which remained so fixed in my memory, and on which I had for so many years so often ruminated with horror, when no one suspected of what I was thinking.

It was pretty, even beautiful; and when I first beheld it, wore the same melancholy expression.

But this almost instantly lighted into a strange fixed smile of recognition.

There was a silence of fully a minute, and then at length *she* spoke; *I* could not.

"How wonderful!" she exclaimed. "Twelve years ago, I saw your face in a dream, and it has haunted me ever since."

"Wonderful indeed!" I repeated, overcoming with an effort the horror that had for a time suspended my utterances. "Twelve years ago, in vision or reality, *I* certainly saw you. I could not forget your face. It has remained before my eyes ever since."

Her smile had softened. Whatever I had fancied strange in it was gone, and it and her dimpling cheeks were now delightfully pretty and intelligent.

I felt reassured, and continued more in the vein which hospitality indicated, to bid her welcome, and to tell her how much pleasure her accidental arrival had given us all, and especially what a happiness it was to me.

I took her hand as I spoke. I was a little shy, as lonely people are, but the situation made me eloquent, and even bold. She pressed my hand, she laid hers upon it, and her eyes glowed, as, looking hastily into mine, she smiled again, and blushed.

She answered my welcome very prettily. I sat down beside her, still wondering; and she said:

"I must tell you my vision about you; it is so very strange that you and I should have had, each of the other so vivid a dream, that each should have seen, I you and you me, looking as we do now, when of course we both were mere children. I was a child, about six years old, and I awoke from a confused and troubled dream, and found myself in a room, unlike my nursery, wainscoted clumsily in some dark wood, and with cupboards and bedsteads, and chairs, and benches placed about it. The beds were, I thought, all empty, and the room itself without anyone but myself in it; and I, after looking about me for some time, and admiring especially an iron candlestick, with two branches, which I should certainly know again, crept under one of the beds to reach the window; but as I got from under the bed, I heard some one crying; and looking up, while I was still upon my knees, I saw *you*—most assuredly you—as I see you now; a beautiful young lady, with golden hair and large blue eyes, and lips—your lips—you, as you are here. Your looks won me; I climbed on the bed and put my arms about you, and I think we both fell asleep. I was aroused by a scream; you were sitting up screaming. I was frightened, and slipped down upon the ground, and, it seemed to me, lost consciousness for a moment; and when I came to myself I was again in my nursery at home. Your face I have never forgotten since. I could not be misled by mere resemblance. You *are* the lady whom I then saw."

It was now my turn to relate my corresponding

vision, which I did, to the undisguised wonder of my new acquaintance.

"I don't know which should be most afraid of the other," she said, again smiling—"If you were less pretty I think I should be very much afraid of you, but being as you are, and you and I both so young, I feel only that I have made your acquaintance twelve years ago, and have already a right to your intimacy; at all events it does seem as if we were destined, from our earliest childhood, to be friends. I wonder whether you feel as strangely drawn towards me as I do to you; I have never had a friend—shall I find one now?" She sighed, and her fine dark eyes gazed passionately on me.

Now the truth is, I felt rather unaccountably towards the beautiful stranger. I did feel, as she said, "drawn towards her," but there was also something of repulsion. In this ambiguous feeling, however, the sense of attraction immensely prevailed. She interested and won me; she was so beautiful and so indescribably engaging.

I perceived now something of languor and exhaustion stealing over her, and hastened to bid her good-night.

"The doctor thinks," I added, "that you ought to have a maid to sit up with you to-night; one of ours is waiting, and you will find her a very useful and quiet creature."

"How kind of you, but I could not sleep, I never could with an attendant in the room. I shan't require any assistance—and, shall I confess my weakness, I am haunted with a terror of robbers. Our house was robbed once, and two servants murdered, so I always lock my door. It has become a habit—and you look so kind I know you will forgive me. I see there is a key in the lock."

She held me close in her pretty arms for a moment and whispered in my ear, "Good-night, darling, it is very hard to part with you, but good-night; to-morrow, but not early, I shall see you again."

She sank back on the pillow with a sigh, and her fine eyes followed me with a fond and melancholy gaze, and she murmured again, "Good-night, dear friend."

Young people like, and even love, on impulse. I was flattered by the evident, though as yet undeserved, fondness she showed me. I liked the confidence with which she at once received me. She was determined that we should be very near friends.

Next day came and we met again. I was delighted with my companion; that is to say, in many respects.

Her looks lost nothing in daylight—she was certainly the most beautiful creature I had ever seen, and the unpleasant remembrance of the face presented in my early dream had lost the effect of the first unexpected recognition.

She confessed that she had experienced a similar shock on seeing me, and precisely the same faint antipathy that had mingled with my admiration of her. We now laughed together over our momentary horrors.

CHAPTER IV
HER HABITS—A SAUNTER

I told you that I was charmed with her in most particulars.

There were some that did not please me so well.

She was above the middle height of women. I shall begin by describing her. She was slender, and wonderfully graceful. Except that her movements were languid—*very* languid—indeed, there was nothing in her appearance to indicate an invalid. Her complexion was rich and brilliant; her features were small and beautifully formed; her eyes large, dark, and lustrous; her hair was quite wonderful, I never saw hair so magnificently thick and long when it was down about her shoulders; I have often placed my hands under it, and laughed with wonder at its weight. It was exquisitely fine and soft, and in colour a rich very dark brown, with something of gold. I loved to let it down, tumbling with its own weight, as, in her room, she lay back in her chair talking in her sweet low voice, I used to fold and braid it, and spread it out and play with it. Heavens! If I had but known all!

I said there were particulars which did not please me. I have told you that her confidence won me the first night I saw her; but I found that she exercised with respect to herself, her mother, her history, everything in fact connected with her life, plans, and people, an ever wakeful reserve. I dare say I was unreasonable, perhaps I was wrong; I dare say I ought to have respected the solemn injunction laid upon my father by the stately lady in black velvet. But curiosity is a restless and unscrupulous passion, and no one girl can endure, with patience, that her's should be baffled by another. What harm could it do anyone to tell me what I so ardently desired to know? Had she no trust in my good sense or honour? Why would she not believe me when I assured her, so solemnly, that I would not divulge one syllable of what she told me to any mortal breathing?

There was a coldness, it seemed to me, beyond her years, in her smiling melancholy persistent refusal to afford me the least ray of light.

I cannot say we quarrelled upon this point, for she would not quarrel upon any. It was, of course, very unfair of me to press her, very ill-bred, but I really could not help it; and I might just as well have let it alone.

What she did tell me amounted, in my unconscionable estimation—to nothing.

It was all summed up in three very vague disclosures:

First.—Her name was Carmilla.

Second.—Her family was very ancient and noble.

Third.—Her home lay in the direction of the west.

She would not tell me the name of her family, nor

their armorial bearings, nor the name of their estate, nor even that of the country they lived in.

You are not to suppose that I worried her incessantly on these subjects. I watched for opportunity, and rather insinuated than urged my inquiries. Once or twice, indeed, I did attack her more directly. But no matter what my tactics, utter failure was invariably the result. Reproaches and caresses were all lost upon her. But I must add this, that her evasion was conducted with so pretty a melancholy and deprecation, with so many, and even passionate declarations of her liking for me, and trust in my honour, and with so many promises that I should at last know all, that I could not find it in my heart long to be offended with her.

She used to place her pretty arms around my neck, draw me to her, and laying her cheek to mine, murmur with her lips near my ear, "Dearest, your little heart is wounded; think me not cruel because I obey the irresistible law of my strength and weakness; if your dear heart is wounded, my wild heart bleeds with yours. In the rapture of my enormous humiliation I live in your warm life, and you shall die—die, sweetly die—into mine. I cannot help it; as I draw near to you, you, in your turn, will draw near to others, and learn the rapture of that cruelty, which yet is love; so, for a while, seek to know no more of me and mine, but trust me with all your loving spirit."

And when she had spoken such a rhapsody, she would press me more closely in her trembling embrace, and her lips in soft kisses gently glow upon my cheek. Her agitations and her language were unintelligible to me.

From these foolish embraces, which were not of very frequent occurrence, I must allow, I used to wish to extricate myself; but my energies seemed to fail me. Her murmured words sounded like a lullaby in my ear, and soothed my resistance into a trance, from which I only seemed to recover myself when she withdrew her arms.

In these mysterious moods I did not like her. I experienced a strange tumultuous excitement that was pleasurable, ever and anon, mingled with a vague sense of fear and disgust. I had no distinct thoughts about her while such scenes lasted, but I was conscious of a love growing into adoration, and also of abhorrence. This I know is a paradox, but I can make no other attempt to explain the feeling.

I now write, after an interval of more than ten years, with a trembling hand, with a confused and horrible recollection of certain occurrences and situations in the ordeal through which I was unconsciously passing; though with a vivid and very sharp remembrance of the main current of my story. But, I suspect, in all lives there are certain emotional scenes, those in which our passions have

been most wildly and terribly roused, that are of all others
the most vaguely and dimly remembered.

Sometimes after an hour of apathy, my strange and
beautiful companion would take my hand and hold it with
a fond pressure, renewed again and again; blushing softly,
gazing in my face with languid and burning eyes, and
breathing so fast that her dress rose and fell with the
tumultuous respiration. It was like the ardour of a lover;
it embarrassed me; it was hateful and yet overpowering;
and with gloating eyes she drew me to her, and her hot
lips travelled along my cheek in kisses; and she would
whisper, almost in sobs, "You are mine, you *shall* be mine,
you and I are one for ever." Then she has thrown herself
back in her chair, with her small hands over her eyes,
leaving me trembling.

"Are we related?" I used to ask. "What can you mean
by all this? I remind you perhaps of some one whom you
love; but you must not, I hate it; I don't know you—I don't
know myself when you look so and talk so."

She used to sigh at my vehemence, then turn away and
drop my hand.

Respecting these very extraordinary manifestations, I
strove in vain to form any satisfactory theory—I could not
refer them to affectation or trick. It was unmistakably the
momentary breaking out of suppressed instinct and emotion.
Was she, notwithstanding her mother's volunteered denial,

subject to brief visitations of insanity; or was there here a disguise and a romance? I had read in old story books of such things. What if a boyish lover had found his way into the house, and sought to prosecute his suit in masquerade, with the assistance of a clever old adventuress? But there were many things against this hypothesis, highly interesting as it was to my vanity.

I could boast of no little attentions such as masculine gallantry delights to offer. Between these passionate moments there were long intervals of common-place, of gaiety, of brooding melancholy, during which, except that I detected her eyes so full of melancholy fire, following me, at times I might have been as nothing to her. Except in these brief periods of mysterious excitement her ways were girlish; and there was always a languor about her, quite incompatible with a masculine system in a state of health.

In some respects her habits were odd. Perhaps not so singular in the opinion of a town lady like you, as they appeared to us rustic people. She used to come down very late, generally not till one o'clock. She would then take a cup of chocolate, but eat nothing; we then went out for a walk, which was a mere saunter, and she seemed, almost immediately, exhausted, and either returned to the schloss or sat on one of the benches that were placed, here and there, among the trees. This was a bodily languor in which her mind did not sympathize. She was always an animated talker, and very intelligent.

She sometimes alluded for a moment to her own home, or mentioned an adventure or situation, or an early recollection, which indicated a people of strange manners, and described customs of which we knew nothing. I gathered from these chance hints that her native country was much more remote than I had at first fancied.

As we sat thus one afternoon under the trees a funeral passed us by. It was that of a pretty young girl, whom I had often seen, the daughter of one of the rangers of the forest. The poor man was walking behind the coffin of his darling; she was his only child, and he looked quite heartbroken. Peasants walking two-and-two came behind, they were singing a funeral hymn.

I rose to mark my respect as they passed, and joined in the hymn they were sweetly singing.

My companion shook me a little roughly, and I turned surprised.

She said brusquely, "Don't you perceive how discordant that is?"

"I think it very sweet, on the contrary," I answered, vexed at the interruption, and very uncomfortable, lest the people who composed the little procession should observe and resent what was passing.

I resumed, therefore, instantly, and again interrupted. "You pierce my ears," said Carmilla, almost angrily, and stopping her ears with her tiny fingers. "Besides, how can you tell that your religion and mine are the same; your forms wound me, and I hate funerals. What a fuss! Why *you* must die—*everyone* must die; and all are happier when they do. Come home."

"My father has gone on with the clergyman to the churchyard. I thought you knew she was to be buried to-day."

"*She?* I don't trouble my head about peasants. I don't know who she is," answered Carmilla, with a flash from her fine eyes.

"She is the poor girl who fancied she saw a ghost a fortnight ago, and has been dying ever since, till yesterday, when she expired."

"Tell me nothing about ghosts. I shan't sleep to-night if you do."

"I hope there is no plague or fever coming; all this looks very like it," I continued. "The swineherd's young wife died only a week ago, and she thought something seized her by the throat as she lay in her bed, and nearly strangled her. Papa says such horrible fancies do accompany some forms of fever. She was quite well the day before. She sank afterwards, and died before a week."

"Well, *her* funeral is over, I hope, and *her* hymn sung; and our ears shan't be tortured with that discord and jargon. It has made me nervous. Sit down here, beside me; sit close; hold my hand; press it hard—hard—harder."

We had moved a little back, and had come to another seat.

She sat down. Her face underwent a change that alarmed and even terrified me for a moment. It darkened, and became horribly livid; her teeth and hands were clenched, and she frowned and compressed her lips, while she stared down upon the ground at her feet, and trembled all over with a continued shudder as irrepressible as ague. All her energies seemed strained to suppress a fit, with which she was then breathlessly tugging; and at length a low convulsive cry of suffering broke from her, and gradually the hysteria subsided. "There! That comes of strangling people with hymns!" she said at last. "Hold me, hold me still. It is passing away."

And so gradually it did; and perhaps to dissipate the somber impression which the spectacle had left upon me, she became unusually animated and chatty; and so we got home.

This was the first time I had seen her exhibit any definable symptoms of that delicacy of health which her mother had spoken of. It was the first time, also, I had seen her exhibit anything like temper.

Both passed away like a summer cloud; and never but once afterwards did I witness on her part a momentary sign of anger. I will tell you how it happened.

She and I were looking out of one of the long drawing-room windows, when there entered the court-yard, over the drawbridge, a figure of a wanderer whom I knew very well. He used to visit the schloss generally twice a year.

It was the figure of a hunchback, with the sharp lean features that generally accompany deformity. He wore a pointed black beard, and he was smiling from ear to ear, showing his white fangs. He was dressed in buff, black, and scarlet, and crossed with more straps and belts than I could count, from which hung all manner of things. Behind, he carried a magic-lantern, and two boxes, which I well knew, in one of which was a salamander, and in the other a mandrake. These monsters used to make my father laugh. They were compounded of parts of monkeys, parrots, squirrels, fish, and hedgehogs, dried and stitched together with great neatness and startling effect. He had a fiddle, a box of conjuring apparatus, a pair of foils and masks attached to his belt, several other mysterious cases dangling about him, and a black staff with copper ferrules in his hand. His companion was a rough spare dog, that followed at his heels, but stopped short suspiciously at the drawbridge, and in a little while began to howl dismally.

In the meantime, the mountebank, standing in the midst of the court-yard, raised his grotesque hat, and made us a very ceremonious bow, paying his compliments very volubly in execrable French, and German not much better.

Then, disengaging his fiddle, he began to scrape a lively air, to which he sang with a merry discord, dancing with ludicrous airs and activity, that made me laugh, in spite of the dog's howling.

Then he advanced to the window with many smiles and salutations, and his hat in his left hand, his fiddle under his arm, and with a fluency that never took breath, he gabbled a long advertisement of all his accomplishments, and the resources of the various arts which he placed at our service, and the curiosities and entertainments which it was in his power, at our bidding, to display.

"Will your ladyships be pleased to buy an amulet against the oupire, which is going like the wolf, I hear, through these woods," he said, dropping his hat on the pavement. "They are dying of it right and left, and here is a charm that never fails; only pinned to the pillow, and you may laugh in his face."

These charms consisted of oblong slips of vellum, with cabalistic ciphers and diagrams upon them.

Carmilla instantly purchased one, and so did I.

He was looking up, and we were smiling down upon him, amused; at least, I can answer for myself. His piercing black eye, as he looked up in our faces, seemed to detect something that fixed for a moment his curiosity.

In an instant he unrolled a leather case, full of all manner of odd little steel instruments.

"See here, my lady," he said, displaying it, and addressing me, "I profess, among other things less useful, the art of dentistry. Plague take that dog!" he interpolated. "Silence, beast! He howls so that your ladyships can scarcely hear a word. Your noble friend, the young lady at your right, has the sharpest tooth,–long, thin, pointed, like an awl, like a needle; ha, ha! With my sharp and long sight, as I look up, I have seen it distinctly; now if it happens to hurt the young lady, and I think it must, here am I, here are my file, my punch, my nippers; I will make it round and blunt, if her ladyship pleases; no longer the tooth of a fish, but of a beautiful young lady as she is. Hey? Is the young lady displeased? Have I been too bold? Have I offended her?"

The young lady, indeed, looked very angry as she drew back from the window.

"How dares that mountebank insult us so? Where is your father? I shall demand redress from him. My father would have had the wretch tied up to the pump, and flogged with a cart-whip, and burnt to the bones with the castle brand!"

She retired from the window a step or two, and sat down, and had hardly lost sight of the offender, when her wrath subsided as suddenly as it had risen, and she gradually recovered her usual tone, and seemed to forget the little hunchback and his follies.

My father was out of spirits that evening. On coming in

he told us that there had been another case very similar to the two fatal ones which had lately occurred. The sister of a young peasant on his estate, only a mile away, was very ill, had been, as she described it, attacked in very nearly the same way, and was now slowly but steadily sinking.

"All this," said my father, "is strictly referable to natural causes. These poor people infect one another with their superstitions, and so repeat in imagination the images of terror that have infested their neighbours."

"But that very circumstance frightens one horribly," said Carmilla.

"How so?" inquired my father.

"I am so afraid of fancying I see such things; I think it would be as bad as reality."

"We are in God's hands; nothing can happen without His permission, and all will end well for those who love Him. He is our faithful creator; He has made us all, and will take care of us."

"Creator! *Nature!*" said the young lady in answer to my gentle father. "And this disease that invades the country is natural. Nature. All things proceed from Nature—don't they? All things in the heaven, in the earth, and under the earth, act and live as Nature ordains? I think so."

"The doctor said he would come here to-day," said my father, after a silence. "I want to know what he thinks about it, and what he thinks we had better do."

"Doctors never did me any good," said Carmilla.

"Then you have been ill?" I asked.

"More ill than ever you were," she answered.

"Long ago?"

"Yes, a long time. I suffered from this very illness; but I forget all but my pain and weakness, and they were not so bad as are suffered in other diseases."

"You were very young then?"

"I dare say; let us talk no more of it. You would not wound a friend?" She looked languidly in my eyes, and passed her arm round my waist lovingly, and led me out of the room. My father was busy over some papers near the window.

"Why does your papa like to frighten us?" said the pretty girl, with a sigh and a little shudder.

"He doesn't, dear Carmilla, it is the very furthest thing from his mind."

"Are you afraid, dearest?"

"I should be very much if I fancied there was any real danger of my being attacked as those poor people were."

"You are afraid to die?"

"Yes, everyone is."

"But to die as lovers may—to die together, so that they may live together. Girls are caterpillars while they live in the world, to be finally butterflies when the summer comes; but in the meantime there are grubs and larvae, don't you see—each with their peculiar propensities, necessities and structure. So says Monsieur Buffon, in his big book, in the next room."

Later in the day the doctor came and was closeted with papa for some time. He was a skillful man, of sixty and upwards. He wore powder, and shaved his pale face as smooth as a pumpkin. He and papa emerged from the room together, and I heard papa laugh, and say as they came out:

"Well, I do wonder at a wise man like you. What do you say to hippogriffs and dragons?"

The doctor was smiling, and made answer, shaking his head—

"Nevertheless life and death are mysterious states, and we know little of the resources of either."

And so they walked on, and I heard no more. I did not then know what the doctor had been broaching, but I think I guess it now.

CHAPTER V
A WONDERFUL LIKENESS

This evening there arrived from Gratz the grave, dark-faced son of the picture cleaner, with a horse and cart laden with two large packing cases, having many pictures in each. It was a journey of ten leagues, and whenever a messenger arrived at the schloss from our little capital of Gratz, we used to crowd about him in the hall, to hear the news.

This arrival created in our secluded quarters quite a sensation. The cases remained in the hall, and the messenger was taken charge of by the servants till he had eaten his supper. Then with assistants, and armed with hammer, ripping-chisel, and turnscrew, he met us in the hall, where we had assembled to witness the unpacking of the cases.

Carmilla sat looking listlessly on, while one after the other the old pictures, nearly all portraits, which had undergone the process of renovation, were brought to light. My mother was of an old Hungarian family, and most of these pictures, which were about to be restored to their places, had come to us through her.

My father had a list in his hand, from which he read, as the artist rummaged out the corresponding numbers. I don't know that the pictures were very good, but they were, undoubtedly, very old, and some of them very curious also. They had, for the most part, the merit of being now seen by me, I may say, for the first time; for the smoke and dust of time had all but obliterated them.

"There is a picture that I have not seen yet," said my father. "In one corner, at the top of it, is the name, as well

as I could read, 'Marcia Karnstein,' and the date '1698';
and I am curious to see how it has turned out."

I remembered it; it was a small picture, about a foot
and a half high, and nearly square, without a frame; but
it was so blackened by age that I could not make it out.

The artist now produced it, with evident pride. It was
quite beautiful; it was startling; it seemed to live. It was the
effigy of Carmilla!

"Carmilla, dear, here is an absolute miracle. Here
you are, living, smiling, ready to speak, in this picture.
Isn't it beautiful, papa? And see, even the little mole on
her throat."

My father laughed, and said, "Certainly it is a wonderful
likeness," but he looked away, and to my surprise seemed
but little struck by it, and went on talking to the picture
cleaner, who was also something of an artist, and discoursed
with intelligence about the portraits or other works, which
his art had just brought into light and colour, while *I*
was more and more lost in wonder the more I looked at
the picture.

"Will you let me hang this picture in my room, papa?"
I asked.

"Certainly, dear," said he, smiling, "I'm very glad you
think it so like. It must be prettier even than I thought it,
if it is."

The young lady did not acknowledge this pretty speech,

did not seem to hear it. She was leaning back in her seat, her fine eyes under their long lashes gazing on me in contemplation, and she smiled in a kind of rapture.

"And now you can read quite plainly the name that is written in the corner. It is not Marcia; it looks as if it was done in gold. The name Mircalla, Countess Karnstein, and this is a little coronet over it, and underneath AD 1698. I am descended from the Karnsteins; that is, mamma was."

"Ah!" said the lady, languidly, "so am I, I think, a very long descent, very ancient. Are there any Karnsteins living now?"

"None who bear the name, I believe. The family were ruined, I believe, in some civil wars, long ago, but the ruins of the castle are only about three miles away."

"How interesting!" she said, languidly. "But see what beautiful moonlight!" She glanced through the hall door, which stood a little open. "Suppose you take a little ramble round the court, and look down at the road and river."

"It is so like the night you came to us," I said.

She sighed, smiling.

She rose, and each with her arm about the other's waist, we walked out upon the pavement.

In silence, slowly we walked down to the drawbridge, where the beautiful landscape opened before us.

"And so you were thinking of the night I came here?" she almost whispered. "Are you glad I came?"

"Delighted, dear Carmilla," I answered.

"And you asked for the picture you think like me, to hang in your room," she murmured with a sigh, as she drew her arm closer about my waist, and let her pretty head sink upon my shoulder.

"How romantic you are, Carmilla," I said. "Whenever you tell me your story, it will be made up chiefly of some one great romance."

She kissed me silently.

"I am sure, Carmilla, you have been in love; that there is, at this moment, an affair of the heart going on."

"I have been in love with no one, and never shall," she whispered, "unless it should be with you."

How beautiful she looked in the moonlight!

Shy and strange was the look with which she quickly hid her face in my neck and hair, with tumultuous sighs, that seemed almost to sob, and pressed in mine a hand that trembled.

Her soft cheek was glowing against mine. "Darling, darling," she murmured, "I live in you; and you would die for me, I love you so."

I started from her.

She was gazing on me with eyes from which all fire, all meaning had flown, and a face colourless and apathetic.

"Is there a chill in the air, dear?" she said drowsily. "I almost shiver; have I been dreaming? Let us come in.

Come; come; come in."

"You look ill, Carmilla; a little faint. You certainly must take some wine," I said.

"Yes, I will. I'm better now. I shall be quite well in a few minutes. Yes, do give me a little wine," answered Carmilla, as we approached the door. "Let us look again for a moment; it is the last time, perhaps, I shall see the moonlight with you."

"How do you feel now, dear Carmilla? Are you really better?" I asked.

I was beginning to take alarm, lest she should have been stricken with the strange epidemic that they said had invaded the country about us.

"Papa would be grieved beyond measure," I added, "if he thought you were ever so little ill, without immediately letting us know. We have a very skillful doctor near this, the physician who was with papa to-day."

"I'm sure he is. I know how kind you all are; but, dear child, I am quite well again. There is nothing ever wrong with me, but a little weakness. People say I am languid; I am incapable of exertion; I can scarcely walk as far as a child of three years old; and every now and then the little strength I have falters, and I become as you have just seen me. But after all I am very easily set up again; in a moment I am perfectly myself. See how I have recovered."

So, indeed, she had; and she and I talked a great deal,

and very animated she was; and the remainder of that
evening passed without any recurrence of what I called
her infatuations. I mean her crazy talk and looks, which
embarrassed, and even frightened me.

But there occurred that night an event which gave my
thoughts quite a new turn, and seemed to startle even
Carmilla's languid nature into momentary energy.

CHAPTER VI
A VERY STRANGE AGONY

When we got into the drawing-room, and had sat down to
our coffee and chocolate, although Carmilla did not take
any, she seemed quite herself again, and Madame, and
Mademoiselle De Lafontaine, joined us, and made a little
card party, in the course of which papa came in for what
he called his "dish of tea."

When the game was over he sat down beside Carmilla
on the sofa, and asked her, a little anxiously, whether she
had heard from her mother since her arrival.

She answered, "No."

He then asked whether she knew where a letter would
reach her at present.

"I cannot tell," she answered ambiguously, "but I have
been thinking of leaving you; you have been already too

hospitable and too kind to me. I have given you an infinity of trouble, and I should wish to take a carriage to-morrow, and post in pursuit of her; I know where I shall ultimately find her, although I dare not tell you."

"But you must not dream of any such thing," exclaimed my father, to my great relief. "We can't afford to lose you so, and I won't consent to your leaving us, except under the care of your mother, who was so good as to consent to your remaining with us till she should herself return. I should be quite happy if I knew that you heard from her; but this evening the accounts of the progress of the mysterious disease that has invaded our neighbourhood grow even more alarming; and my beautiful guest, I do feel the responsibility, unaided by advice from your mother, very much. But I shall do my best; and one thing is certain, that you must not think of leaving us without her distinct direction to that effect. We should suffer too much in parting from you to consent to it easily."

"Thank you, sir, a thousand times for your hospitality," she answered, smiling bashfully. "You have all been too kind to me; I have seldom been so happy in all my life before, as in your beautiful château, under your care, and in the society of your dear daughter."

So he gallantly, in his old-fashioned way, kissed her hand, smiling and pleased at her little speech.

I accompanied Carmilla as usual to her room, and sat

and chatted with her while she was preparing for bed.

"Do you think," I said at length, "that you will ever confide fully in me?"

She turned round smiling, but made no answer, only continued to smile on me.

"You won't answer that?" I said. "You can't answer pleasantly; I ought not to have asked you."

"You were quite right to ask me that, or anything. You do not know how dear you are to me, or you could not think any confidence too great to look for. But I am under vows, no nun half so awfully, and I dare not tell my story yet, even to you. The time is very near when you shall know everything. You will think me cruel, very selfish, but love is always selfish; the more ardent the more selfish. How jealous I am you cannot know. You must come with me, loving me, to death; or else hate me and still come with me, and *hating* me through death and after. There is no such word as indifference in my apathetic nature."

"Now, Carmilla, you are going to talk your wild nonsense again," I said hastily.

"Not I, silly little fool as I am, and full of whims and fancies; for your sake I'll talk like a sage. Were you ever at a ball?"

"No; how you do run on. What is it like? How charming it must be."

"I almost forget, it is years ago."

I laughed.

"You are not so old. Your first ball can hardly be forgotten yet."

"I remember everything about it—with an effort. I see it all, as divers see what is going on above them, through a medium, dense, rippling, but transparent. There occurred that night what has confused the picture, and made its colours faint. I was all but assassinated in my bed, wounded *here*," she touched her breast, "and never was the same since."

"Were you near dying?"

"Yes, very—a cruel love—strange love, that would have taken my life. Love will have its sacrifices. No sacrifice without blood. Let us go to sleep now; I feel so lazy. How can I get up just now and lock my door?"

She was lying with her tiny hands buried in her rich wavy hair, under her cheek, her little head upon the pillow, and her glittering eyes followed me wherever I moved, with a kind of shy smile that I could not decipher.

I bid her good-night, and crept from the room with an uncomfortable sensation.

I often wondered whether our pretty guest ever said her prayers. *I* certainly had never seen her upon her knees. In the morning she never came down until long after our family prayers were over, and at night she never left the drawing-room to attend our brief evening prayers in the hall.

If it had not been that it had casually come out in one of our careless talks that she had been baptized, I should have doubted her being a Christian. Religion was a subject on which I had never heard her speak a word. If I had known the world better, this particular neglect or antipathy would not have so much surprised me. The precautions of nervous people are infectious, and persons of a like temperament are pretty sure, after a time, to imitate them. I had adopted Carmilla's habit of locking her bed-room door, having taken into my head all her whimsical alarms about midnight invaders and prowling assassins. I had also adopted her precaution of making a brief search through her room, to satisfy herself that no lurking assassin or robber was "ensconced."

These wise measures taken, I got into my bed and fell asleep. A light was burning in my room. This was an old habit, of very early date, and which nothing could have tempted me to dispense with.

Thus fortified I might take my rest in peace. But dreams come through stone walls, light up dark rooms, or darken light ones, and their persons make their exits and their entrances as they please, and laugh at locksmiths.

I had a dream that night that was the beginning of a very strange agony.

I cannot call it a nightmare, for I was quite conscious of being asleep. But I was equally conscious of being in my room, and lying in bed, precisely as I actually was. I saw, or fancied I saw, the room and its furniture just as I had seen it last, except that it was very dark, and I saw something moving round the foot of the bed, which at first I could not accurately distinguish. But I soon saw that it was a sooty-black animal that resembled a monstrous cat. It appeared to me about four or five feet long, for it measured fully the length of the hearth-rug as it passed over it; and it continued toing and froing with the lithe sinister restlessness of a beast in a cage. I could not cry out, although as you may suppose, I was terrified. Its pace was growing faster, and the room rapidly darker and darker, and at length so dark that I could no longer see anything of it but its eyes. I felt it spring lightly on the bed. The two broad eyes approached my face, and suddenly I felt a stinging pain as if two large needles darted, an inch or two apart, deep into my breast. I waked with a scream. The room was lighted by the candle that burnt there all through the night, and I saw a female figure standing at the foot of the bed, a little at the right side. It was in a dark loose dress, and its hair was down and covered its shoulders. A block of stone could not have been more still. There was not the slightest stir of respiration. As I stared at it, the figure appeared to have changed its place, and was now nearer the door; then, close to it, the door opened, and it passed out.

I was now relieved, and able to breathe and move. My first thought was that Carmilla had been playing me a trick, and that I had forgotten to secure my door. I hastened to it, and found it locked as usual on the inside. I was afraid to open it—I was horrified. I sprang into my bed and covered my head up in the bed-clothes, and lay there more dead than alive till morning.

CHAPTER VII
DESCENDING

It would be vain my attempting to tell you the horror with which, even now, I recall the occurrence of that night. It was no such transitory terror as a dream leaves behind it. It seemed to deepen by time, and communicated itself to the room and the very furniture that had encompassed the apparition.

I could not bear next day to be alone for a moment. I should have told papa, but for two opposite reasons. At one time I thought he would laugh at my story, and I could not bear its being treated as a jest; and at another, I thought he might fancy that I had been attacked by the mysterious complaint which had invaded our neighbourhood. I had myself no misgivings of the kind, and as he had been rather an invalid for some time, I was afraid of alarming him.

I was comfortable enough with my good-natured companions, Madame Perrodon and the vivacious Mademoiselle De Lafontaine. They both perceived that I was out of spirits and nervous, and at length I told them what lay so heavy at my heart.

Mademoiselle laughed, but I fancied that Madame Perrodon looked anxious.

"By-the-by," said Mademoiselle, laughing, "the long lime-tree walk, behind Carmilla's bed-room window, is haunted!"

"Nonsense!" exclaimed Madame, who probably thought the theme rather inopportune, "and who tells that story, my dear?"

"Martin says that he came up twice, when the old yard-gate was being repaired, before sunrise, and twice saw the same female figure walking down the lime-tree avenue."

"So he well might, as long as there are cows to milk in the river fields," said Madame.

"I daresay; but Martin chooses to be frightened, and never did I see fool *more* frightened."

"You must not say a word about it to Carmilla, because she can see down that walk from her room window," I interposed, "and she is, if possible, a greater coward than I."

Carmilla came down rather later than usual that day.

"I was so frightened last night," she said, so soon as we were together, "and I am sure I should have seen something dreadful if it had not been for that charm I bought from the poor little hunchback whom I called such hard names. I had a dream of something black coming round my bed, and I awoke in a perfect horror, and I really thought, for some seconds, I saw a dark figure near the chimney-piece, but I felt under my pillow for my charm, and the moment my fingers touched it, the figure disappeared, and I felt quite certain, only that I had it by me, that something frightful would have made its appearance, and, perhaps, throttled me, as it did those poor people we heard of."

"Well, listen to me," I began, and recounted my adventure, at the recital of which she appeared horrified.

"And had you the charm near you?" she asked, earnestly.

"No, I had dropped it into a china vase in the drawing-room, but I shall certainly take it with me to-night, as you have so much faith in it."

At this distance of time I cannot tell you, or even understand, how I overcame my horror so effectually as to lie alone in my room that night. I remember distinctly that I pinned the charm to my pillow. I fell asleep almost immediately, and slept even more soundly than usual all night.

Next night I passed as well. My sleep was delightfully deep and dreamless. But I wakened with a sense of lassitude and melancholy, which, however, did not exceed a degree that was almost luxurious.

"Well, I told you so," said Carmilla, when I described my quiet sleep, "I had such delightful sleep myself last night; I pinned the charm to the breast of my night-dress. It was too far away the night before. I am quite sure it was all fancy, except the dreams. I used to think that evil spirits made dreams, but our doctor told me it is no such thing. Only a fever passing by, or some other malady, as they often do, he said, knocks at the door, and not being able to get in, passes on, with that alarm."

"And what do you think the charm is?" said I.

"It has been fumigated or immersed in some drug, and is an antidote against the malaria," she answered.

"Then it acts only on the body?"

"Certainly; you don't suppose that evil spirits are frightened by bits of ribbon, or the perfumes of a druggist's shop? No, these complaints, wandering in the air, begin by trying the nerves, and so infect the brain, but before they can seize upon you, the antidote repels them. That I am sure is what the charm has done for us. It is nothing magical, it is simply natural."

I should have been happier if I could have quite agreed with Carmilla, but I did my best, and the impression was a little losing its force.

For some nights I slept profoundly; but still every morning I felt the same lassitude, and a languor weighed upon me all day. I felt myself a changed girl. A strange melancholy was stealing over me, a melancholy that I would not have interrupted. Dim thoughts of death began to open, and an idea that I was slowly sinking took gentle, and, somehow, not unwelcome possession of me. If it was sad, the tone of mind which this induced was also sweet. Whatever it might be, my soul acquiesced in it.

I would not admit that I was ill, I would not consent to tell my papa, or to have the doctor sent for.

Carmilla became more devoted to me than ever, and her strange paroxysms of languid adoration more frequent. She used to gloat on me with increasing ardour the more my strength and spirits waned. This always shocked me like a momentary glare of insanity.

Without knowing it, I was now in a pretty advanced stage of the strangest illness under which mortal ever suffered. There was an unaccountable fascination in its earlier symptoms that more than reconciled me to the incapacitating effect of that stage of the malady. This fascination increased for a time, until it reached a certain point, when gradually a sense of the horrible mingled itself with it, deepening, as you shall hear, until it discoloured and perverted the whole state of my life.

The first change I experienced was rather agreeable. It was very near the turning point from which began the descent to Avernus.

Certain vague and strange sensations visited me in my sleep. The prevailing one was of that pleasant, peculiar cold thrill which we feel in bathing, when we move against the current of a river. This was soon accompanied by dreams that seemed interminable, and were so vague that I could never recollect their scenery and persons, or any one connected portion of their action. But they left an awful impression, and a sense of exhaustion, as if I had passed through a long period of great mental exertion and danger. After all these dreams there remained on waking a remembrance of having been in a place very nearly dark, and of having spoken to people whom I could not see; and especially of one clear voice, of a female's, very deep, that spoke as if at a distance, slowly, and producing always the same sensation of indescribable solemnity and fear. Sometimes there came a sensation as if a hand was drawn softly along my cheek and neck. Sometimes it was as if warm lips kissed me, and longer and more lovingly as they reached my throat, but there the caress fixed itself. My heart beat faster, my breathing rose and fell rapidly and full drawn; a sobbing, that rose into a sense of strangulation, supervened, and turned into a dreadful convulsion, in which my senses left me and I became unconscious.

It was now three weeks since the commencement of this unaccountable state. My sufferings had, during the last week, told upon my appearance. I had grown pale, my eyes were dilated and darkened underneath, and the languor which I had long felt began to display itself in my countenance.

My father asked me often whether I was ill; but, with an obstinacy which now seems to me unaccountable, I persisted in assuring him that I was quite well.

In a sense this was true. I had no pain, I could complain of no bodily derangement. My complaint seemed to be one of the imagination, or the nerves, and, horrible as my sufferings were, I kept them, with a morbid reserve, very nearly to myself.

It could not be that terrible complaint which the peasants called the oupire, for I had now been suffering for three weeks, and they were seldom ill for much more than three days, when death put an end to their miseries.

Carmilla complained of dreams and feverish sensations, but by no means of so alarming a kind as mine. I say that mine were extremely alarming. Had I been capable of comprehending my condition, I would have invoked aid and advice on my knees. The narcotic of an unsuspected influence was acting upon me, and my perceptions were benumbed.

I am going to tell you now of a dream that led immediately to an odd discovery.

One night, instead of the voice I was accustomed to hear in the dark, I heard one, sweet and tender, and at the same time terrible, which said, "Your mother warns you to beware of the assassin." At the same time a light unexpectedly sprang up, and I saw Carmilla, standing, near the foot of my bed, in her white night-dress, bathed, from her chin to her feet, in one great stain of blood.

I wakened with a shriek, possessed with the one idea that Carmilla was being murdered. I remember springing from my bed, and my next recollection is that of standing in the lobby, crying for help.

Madame and Mademoiselle came scurrying out of their rooms in alarm; a lamp burned always on the lobby, and seeing me, they soon learned the cause of my terror.

I insisted on our knocking at Carmilla's door. Our knocking was unanswered. It soon became a pounding and an uproar. We shrieked her name, but all was in vain.

We all grew frightened, for the door was locked. We hurried back, in panic, to my room. There we rang the bell long and furiously. If my father's room had been at that side of the house, we would have called him up at once to our aid. But, alas! he was quite out of hearing, and to reach him involved an excursion for which we none of us had the courage.

Servants, however, soon came running up the stairs; I had got on my dressing-gown and slippers meanwhile, and my companions were already similarly furnished. Recognizing the voices of the servants on the lobby, we sallied out together; and having renewed, as fruitlessly, our summons at Carmilla's door, I ordered the men to force the lock. They did so, and we stood, holding our lights aloft, in the doorway, and so stared into the room.

We called her by name; but there was still no reply. We looked round the room. Everything was undisturbed. It was exactly in the state in which I had left it on bidding her good-night. But Carmilla was gone.

CHAPTER VIII
SEARCH

At the sight of the room, perfectly undisturbed except for our violent entrance, we began to cool a little, and soon recovered our senses sufficiently to dismiss the men. It had struck Mademoiselle that possibly Carmilla had been wakened by the uproar at her door, and in her first panic had jumped from her bed, and hid herself in a press, or behind a curtain, from which she could not, of course, emerge until the majordomo and his myrmidons had withdrawn. We now recommenced our search, and began to call her by name again.

It was all to no purpose. Our perplexity and agitation increased. We examined the windows, but they were secured. I implored of Carmilla, if she had concealed herself, to play this cruel trick no longer—to come out, and to end our anxieties. It was all useless. I was by this time convinced that she was not in the room, nor in the dressing-room, the door of which was still locked on this side. She could not have passed it. I was utterly puzzled. Had Carmilla discovered one of those secret passages which the old housekeeper said were known to exist in the schloss, although the tradition of their exact situation had been lost? A little time would, no doubt, explain all—utterly perplexed as, for the present, we were.

It was past four o'clock, and I preferred passing the remaining hours of darkness in Madame's room. Daylight brought no solution of the difficulty.

The whole household, with my father at its head, was in a state of agitation next morning. Every part of the château was searched. The grounds were explored. Not a trace of the missing lady could be discovered. The stream was about to be dragged; my father was in distraction; what a tale to have to tell the poor girl's mother on her return. I, too, was almost beside myself, though my grief was quite of a different kind.

The morning was passed in alarm and excitement. It was now one o'clock, and still no tidings. I ran up to Carmilla's room, and found her standing at her dressing-table. I was astounded. I could not believe my eyes. She beckoned me to her with her pretty finger, in silence. Her face expressed extreme fear.

I ran to her in an ecstasy of joy; I kissed and embraced her again and again. I ran to the bell and rang it vehemently, to bring others to the spot, who might at once relieve my father's anxiety.

"Dear Carmilla, what has become of you all this time? We have been in agonies of anxiety about you," I exclaimed. "Where have you been? How did you come back?"

"Last night has been a night of wonders," she said.

"For mercy's sake, explain all you can."

"It was past two last night," she said, "when I went to sleep as usual in my bed, with my doors locked, that of the dressing-room, and that opening upon the gallery. My sleep was uninterrupted and, so far as I know, dreamless; but I awoke just now on the sofa in the dressing-room there, and I found the door between the rooms open, and the other door forced. How could all this have happened without my being wakened? It must have been accompanied with a great deal of noise, and I am particularly easily wakened; and how could I have been carried out of my bed without my sleep having been interrupted, I whom the slightest stir startles?"

By this time, Madame, Mademoiselle, my father, and a number of the servants were in the room. Carmilla was, of course, overwhelmed with inquiries, congratulations, and welcomes. She had but one story to tell, and seemed the least able of all the party to suggest any way of accounting for what had happened.

My father took a turn up and down the room, thinking. I saw Carmilla's eye follow him for a moment with a sly, dark glance.

When my father had sent the servants away, Mademoiselle having gone in search of a little bottle of valerian and salvolatile, and there being no one now in the room with Carmilla, except my father, Madame, and myself, he came to her thoughtfully, took her hand very kindly, led her to the sofa, and sat down beside her.

"Will you forgive me, my dear, if I risk a conjecture, and ask a question?"

"Who can have a better right?" she said. "Ask what you please, and I will tell you everything. But my story is simply one of bewilderment and darkness. I know absolutely nothing. Put any question you please. But you know, of course, the limitations mamma has placed me under."

"Perfectly, my dear child. I need not approach the topics on which she desires our silence. Now, the marvel of last night consists in your having been moved from your bed and your room, without being wakened, and this removal having occurred apparently while the windows were still secured, and the two doors locked on the inside. I will tell you my theory, and first ask you a question."

Carmilla was leaning on her hand dejectedly; Madame

and I were listening breathlessly.

"Now, my question is this. Have you ever been suspected of walking in your sleep?"

"Never, since I was very young indeed."

"But you did walk in your sleep when you were young?"

"Yes; I know I did. I have been told so often by my old nurse."

My father smiled and nodded.

"Well, what has happened is this. You got up in your sleep, unlocked the door, not leaving the key, as usual, in the lock, but taking it out and locking it on the outside; you again took the key out, and carried it away with you to some one of the five-and-twenty rooms on this floor, or perhaps up-stairs or down-stairs. There are so many rooms and closets, so much heavy furniture, and such accumulations of lumber, that it would require a week to search this old house thoroughly. Do you see, now, what I mean?"

"I do, but not all," she answered.

"And how, papa, do you account for her finding herself on the sofa in the dressing-room, which we had searched so carefully?"

"She came there after you had searched it, still in her sleep, and at last awoke spontaneously, and was as much surprised to find herself where she was as anyone else. I wish all mysteries were as easily and innocently explained as yours, Carmilla," he said, laughing. "And so we may congratulate ourselves on the certainty that the most natural explanation of the occurrence is one that involves no drugging, no tampering with locks, no burglars, or poisoners, or witches—nothing that need alarm Carmilla, or anyone else, for our safety."

Carmilla was looking charmingly. Nothing could be more beautiful than her tints. Her beauty was, I think, enhanced by that graceful languor that was peculiar to her. I think my father was silently contrasting her looks with mine, for he said:

"I wish my poor Laura was looking more like herself"; and he sighed.

So our alarms were happily ended, and Carmilla restored to her friends.

CHAPTER IX

THE DOCTOR

As Carmilla would not hear of an attendant sleeping in her room, my father arranged that a servant should sleep outside her door, so that she could not attempt to make another such excursion without being arrested at her own door.

That night passed quietly; and next morning early, the doctor, whom my father had sent for without telling me a word about it, arrived to see me.

Madame accompanied me to the library; and there the grave little doctor, with white hair and spectacles, whom I mentioned before, was waiting to receive me.

I told him my story, and as I proceeded he grew graver and graver.

We were standing, he and I, in the recess of one of the windows, facing one another. When my statement was over, he leaned his shoulders against the wall, and with his eyes fixed on me earnestly, with an interest in which was a dash of horror.

After a minute's reflection, he asked Madame if he could see my father.

He was sent for accordingly, and as he entered, smiling, he said:

"I dare say, doctor, you are going to tell me that I am an old fool for having brought you here; I hope I am."

But his smile faded into shadow as the doctor, with a very grave face, beckoned him to him.

He and the doctor talked for some time in the same recess where I had just conferred with the physician. It seemed an earnest and argumentative conversation. The room is very large, and I and Madame stood together, burning with curiosity, at the further end. Not a word could we hear, however, for they spoke in a very low tone, and the deep recess of the window quite concealed the doctor from view, and very nearly my father, whose foot, arm, and shoulder only could we see; and the voices were, I suppose, all the less audible for the sort of closet which the thick wall and window formed.

After a time my father's face looked into the room; it was pale, thoughtful, and, I fancied, agitated.

"Laura, dear, come here for a moment. Madame, we shan't trouble you, the doctor says, at present."

Accordingly I approached, for the first time a little alarmed; for, although I felt very weak, I did not feel ill; and strength, one always fancies, is a thing that may be picked up when we please.

My father held out his hand to me, as I drew near, but he was looking at the doctor, and he said:

"It certainly *is* very odd; I don't understand it quite. Laura, come here, dear; now attend to Doctor Spielsberg, and recollect yourself."

"You mentioned a sensation like that of two needles piercing the skin, somewhere about your neck, on the night when you experienced your first horrible dream. Is there still any soreness?"

"None at all," I answered.

"Can you indicate with your finger about the point at which you think this occurred?"

"Very little below my throat—*here*," I answered.

I wore a morning dress, which covered the place I

pointed to.

"Now you can satisfy yourself," said the doctor. "You won't mind your papa's lowering your dress a very little. It is necessary, to detect a symptom of the complaint under which you have been suffering."

I acquiesced. It was only an inch or two below the edge of my collar.

"God bless me!—so it is," exclaimed my father, growing pale.

"You see it now with your own eyes," said the doctor, with a gloomy triumph.

"What is it?" I exclaimed, beginning to be frightened.

"Nothing, my dear young lady, but a small blue spot, about the size of the tip of your little finger, and now," he continued, turning to papa, "the question is, what is best to be done?"

"Is there any danger?" I urged, in great trepidation.

"I trust not, my dear," answered the doctor. "I don't see why you should not recover. I don't see why you should not begin *immediately* to get better. That is the point at which the sense of strangulation begins?"

"Yes," I answered.

"And—recollect as well as you can—the same point was a kind of centre of that thrill which you described just now, like the current of a cold stream running against you?"

"It may have been; I think it was."

"Ay, you see?" he added, turning to my father. "Shall I say a word to Madame?"

"Certainly," said my father.

He called Madame to him, and said:

"I find my young friend here far from well. It won't be of any great consequence, I hope; but it will be necessary that some steps be taken, which I will explain by-and-by; but in the meantime, Madame, you will be so good as not to let Miss Laura be alone for one moment. That is the only direction I need give for the present. It is indispensable."

"We may rely upon your kindness, Madame, I know," added my father.

Madame satisfied him eagerly.

"And you, dear Laura, I know you will observe the doctor's direction."

"I shall have to ask your opinion upon another patient, whose symptoms slightly resemble those of my daughter, that have just been detailed to you—very much milder in degree, but I believe quite of the same sort. She is a young lady—our guest; but as you say you will be passing this way again this evening, you can't do better than take your supper here, and you can then see her. She does not come down till the afternoon."

"I thank you," said the doctor. "I shall be with you, then, at about seven this evening."

And then they repeated their directions to me and to Madame, and with this parting charge my father left us, and walked out with the doctor; and I saw them pacing together up and down between the road and the moat, on the grassy platform in front of the castle, evidently absorbed in earnest conversation.

The doctor did not return. I saw him mount his horse there, take his leave, and ride away eastward through the forest.

Nearly at the same time I saw the man arrive from Dranfeld with the letters, and dismount and hand the bag to my father.

In the meantime, Madame and I were both busy, lost in conjecture as to the reasons of the singular and earnest direction which the doctor and my father had concurred in imposing. Madame, as she afterwards told me, was afraid the doctor apprehended a sudden seizure, and that, without prompt assistance, I might either lose my life in a fit, or at least be seriously hurt.

This interpretation did not strike me; and I fancied, perhaps luckily for my nerves, that the arrangement was prescribed simply to secure a companion, who would prevent my taking too much exercise, or eating unripe fruit, or doing any of the fifty foolish things to which young people are supposed to be prone.

About half-an-hour after, my father came in—he had a

letter in his hand—and said:

"This letter has been delayed; it is from General Spielsdorf. He might have been here yesterday, he may not come till to-morrow, or he may be here to-day."

He put the open letter into my hand; but he did not look pleased, as he used when a guest, especially one so much loved as the General, was coming. On the contrary, he looked as if he wished him at the bottom of the Red Sea. There was plainly something on his mind which he did not choose to divulge.

"Papa, darling, will you tell me this?" said I, suddenly laying my hand on his arm, and looking, I am sure, imploringly in his face.

"Perhaps," he answered, smoothing my hair caressingly over my eyes.

"Does the doctor think me very ill?"

"No, dear; he thinks, if the right steps are taken, you will be quite well again, at least, on the high road to a complete recovery, in a day or two," he answered, a little drily. "I wish our good friend, the General, had chosen any other time; that is, I wish you had been perfectly well to receive him."

"But do tell me, papa," I insisted, "*what* does he think is the matter with me?"

"Nothing; you must not plague me with questions," he answered, with more irritation than I ever remember him to have displayed before; and seeing that I looked wounded, I suppose, he kissed me, and added, "You shall know all about it in a day or two; that is, all that *I* know. In the meantime you are not to trouble your head about it."

He turned and left the room, but came back before I had done wondering and puzzling over the oddity of all this; it was merely to say that he was going to Karnstein, and had ordered the carriage to be ready at twelve, and that I and Madame should accompany him; he was going to see the priest who lived near those picturesque grounds, upon business, and as Carmilla had never seen them, she could follow, when she came down, with Mademoiselle, who would bring materials for what you call a pic-nic, which might be laid for us in the ruined castle.

At twelve o'clock, accordingly, I was ready, and not long after, my father, Madame and I set out upon our projected drive.

Passing the drawbridge we turn to the right, and follow the road over the steep Gothic bridge, westward, to reach the deserted village and ruined castle of Karnstein.

No sylvan drive can be fancied prettier. The ground breaks into gentle hills and hollows, all clothed with beautiful woods, totally destitute of the comparative formality which artificial planting and early culture and pruning impart.

The irregularities of the ground often lead the road out

of its course, and cause it to wind beautifully round the sides of broken hollows and the steeper sides of the hills, among varieties of ground almost inexhaustible.

Turning one of these points, we suddenly encountered our old friend, the General, riding towards us, attended by a mounted servant. His portmanteaus were following in a hired waggon, such as we term a cart.

The General dismounted as we pulled up, and, after the usual greetings, was easily persuaded to accept the vacant seat in the carriage, and send his horse on with his servant to the schloss.

CHAPTER X
BEREAVED

It was about ten months since we had last seen him; but that time had sufficed to make an alteration of years in his appearance. He had grown thinner; something of gloom and anxiety had taken the place of that cordial serenity which used to characterize his features. His dark blue eyes, always penetrating, now gleamed with a sterner light from under his shaggy grey eyebrows. It was not such a change as grief alone usually induces, and angrier passions seemed to have had their share in bringing it about.

We had not long resumed our drive, when the General

began to talk, with his usual soldierly directness, of the bereavement, as he termed it, which he had sustained in the death of his beloved niece and ward; and then broke out in a tone of intense bitterness and fury, inveighing against the "hellish arts" to which she had fallen a victim, and expressing, with more exasperation than piety, his wonder that Heaven should tolerate so monstrous an indulgence of the lusts and malignity of hell.

My father, who saw at once that something very extraordinary had befallen, asked him, if not too painful to him, to detail the circumstances which he thought justified the strong terms in which he expressed himself.

"I should tell you all with pleasure," said the General, "but you would not believe me."

"Why should I not?" he asked.

"Because," he answered testily, "you believe in nothing but what consists with your own prejudices and illusions. I remember when I was like you, but I have learned better."

"Try me," said my father; "I am not such a dogmatist as you suppose. Besides which, I very well know that you generally require proof for what you believe, and am, therefore, very strongly pre-disposed to respect your conclusions."

"You are right in supposing that I have not been led lightly into a belief in the marvellous—for what I have experienced *is* marvellous—and I have been forced by extraordinary evidence to credit that which ran counter, diametrically, to all my theories. I have been made the dupe of a preternatural conspiracy."

Notwithstanding his professions of confidence in the General's penetration, I saw my father, at this point, glance at the General, with, as I thought, a marked suspicion of his sanity.

The General did not see it, luckily. He was looking gloomily and curiously into the glades and vistas of the woods that were opening before us.

"You are going to the ruins of Karnstein?" he said. "Yes, it is a lucky coincidence; do you know I was going to ask you to bring me there to inspect them. I have a special object in exploring. There is a ruined chapel, ain't there, with a great many tombs of that extinct family?"

"So there are—highly interesting," said my father. "I hope you are thinking of claiming the title and estates?"

My father said this gaily, but the General did not recollect the laugh, or even the smile, which courtesy exacts for a friend's joke; on the contrary, he looked grave and even fierce, ruminating on a matter that stirred his anger and horror.

"Something very different," he said, gruffly. "I mean to unearth some of those fine people. I hope, by God's blessing, to accomplish a pious sacrilege here, which will relieve our earth of certain monsters, and enable honest people to sleep in their beds without being assailed by murderers. I have strange things to tell you, my dear friend, such as I myself would have scouted as incredible a few months since."

My father looked at him again, but this time not with a glance of suspicion—with an eye, rather, of keen intelligence and alarm.

"The house of Karnstein," he said, "has been long extinct: a hundred years at least. My dear wife was maternally descended from the Karnsteins. But the name and title have long ceased to exist. The castle is a ruin; the very village is deserted; it is fifty years since the smoke of a chimney was seen there; not a roof left."

"Quite true. I have heard a great deal about that since I last saw you; a great deal that will astonish you. But I had better relate everything in the order in which it occurred," said the General. "You saw my dear ward—my child, I may call her. No creature could have been more beautiful, and only three months ago none more blooming."

"Yes, poor thing! when I saw her last she certainly was quite lovely," said my father. "I was grieved and shocked more than I can tell you, my dear friend; I knew what a blow it was to you."

He took the General's hand, and they exchanged a kind pressure. Tears gathered in the old soldier's eyes. He did not seek to conceal them. He said:

"We have been very old friends; I knew you would

feel for me, childless as I am. She had become an object of very near interest to me, and repaid my care by an affection that cheered my home and made my life happy. That is all gone. The years that remain to me on earth may not be very long; but by God's mercy I hope to accomplish a service to mankind before I die, and to subserve the vengeance of Heaven upon the fiends who have murdered my poor child in the spring of her hopes and beauty!"

"You said, just now, that you intended relating everything as it occurred," said my father. "Pray do; I assure you that it is not mere curiosity that prompts me."

By this time we had reached the point at which the Drunstall road, by which the General had come, diverges from the road which we were travelling to Karnstein.

"How far is it to the ruins?" inquired the General, looking anxiously forward.

"About half a league," answered my father. "Pray let us hear the story you were so good as to promise."

CHAPTER XI
THE STORY

"With all my heart," said the General, with an effort; and after a short pause in which to arrange his subject, he commenced one of the strangest narratives I ever heard.

"My dear child was looking forward with great pleasure to the visit you had been so good as to arrange for her to your charming daughter." Here he made me a gallant but melancholy bow. "In the meantime we had an invitation to my old friend the Count Carlsfeld, whose schloss is about six leagues to the other side of Karnstein. It was to attend the series of fêtes which, you remember, were given by him in honour of his illustrious visitor, the Grand Duke Charles."

"Yes; and very splendid, I believe, they were," said my father.

"Princely! But then his hospitalities are quite regal. He has Aladdin's lamp. The night from which my sorrow dates was devoted to a magnificent masquerade. The grounds were thrown open, the trees hung with coloured lamps. There was such a display of fireworks as Paris itself had never witnessed. And such music—music, you know, is my weakness—such ravishing music! The finest instrumental band, perhaps, in the world, and the finest singers who could be collected from all the great operas in Europe. As you wandered through these fantastically illuminated grounds, the moon-lighted château throwing a rosy light from its long rows of windows, you would suddenly hear these ravishing voices stealing from the silence of some grove, or rising from boats upon the lake. I felt myself, as I looked and listened, carried back into the romance and poetry of my early youth.

"When the fireworks were ended, and the ball beginning, we returned to the noble suite of rooms that were thrown open to the dancers. A masked ball, you know, is a beautiful sight; but so brilliant a spectacle of the kind I never saw before.

"It was a very aristocratic assembly. I was myself almost the only 'nobody' present.

"My dear child was looking quite beautiful. She wore no mask. Her excitement and delight added an unspeakable charm to her features, always lovely. I remarked a young lady, dressed magnificently, but wearing a mask, who appeared to me to be observing my ward with extraordinary interest. I had seen her, earlier in the evening, in the great hall, and again, for a few minutes, walking near us, on the terrace under the castle windows, similarly employed. A lady, also masked, richly and gravely dressed, and with a stately air, like a person of rank, accompanied her as a chaperon. Had the young lady not worn a mask, I could, of course, have been much more certain upon the question whether she was really watching my poor darling. I am now well assured that she was.

"We were now in one of the *salons*. My poor dear child had been dancing, and was resting a little in one of the chairs near the door; I was standing near. The two ladies I have mentioned had approached, and the younger took the chair next my ward; while her companion stood beside me, and for a little time addressed herself, in a low tone, to her charge.

"Availing herself of the privilege of her mask, she turned to me, and in the tone of an old friend, and calling me by my name, opened a conversation with me, which piqued my curiosity a good deal. She referred to many scenes where she had met me—at Court, and at distinguished houses. She alluded to little incidents which I had long ceased to think of, but which, I found, had only lain in abeyance in my memory, for they instantly started into life at her touch.

"I became more and more curious to ascertain who she was, every moment. She parried my attempts to discover very adroitly and pleasantly. The knowledge she showed of many passages in my life seemed to me all but unaccountable; and she appeared to take a not unnatural pleasure in foiling my curiosity, and in seeing me flounder, in my eager perplexity, from one conjecture to another.

"In the meantime the young lady, whom her mother called by the odd name of Millarca, when she once or twice addressed her, had, with the same ease and grace, got into conversation with my ward.

"She introduced herself by saying that her mother was a very old acquaintance of mine. She spoke of the agreeable audacity which a mask rendered practicable; she talked like a friend; she admired her dress, and insinuated very prettily her admiration of her beauty. She amused her with laughing criticisms upon the people who crowded the ballroom, and laughed at my poor child's fun. She was very witty and lively when she pleased, and after a time they had grown very good friends, and the young stranger lowered her mask, displaying a remarkably beautiful face. I had never seen it before, neither had my dear child. But though it was new to us, the features were so engaging, as well as lovely, that it was impossible not to feel the attraction powerfully. My poor girl did so. I never saw anyone more taken with another at first sight, unless, indeed, it was the stranger herself, who seemed quite to have lost her heart to her.

"In the meantime, availing myself of the licence of a masquerade, I put not a few questions to the elder lady.

"'You have puzzled me utterly,' I said, laughing. 'Is that not enough? Won't you, now, consent to stand on equal terms, and do me the kindness to remove your mask?'

"'Can any request be more unreasonable?' she replied. 'Ask a lady to yield an advantage! Beside, how do you know you should recognize me? Years make changes.'

"'As you see,' I said, with a bow, and, I suppose, a rather melancholy little laugh.

"'As philosophers tell us,' she said; 'and how do you know that a sight of my face would help you?'

"'I should take chance for that,' I answered. 'It is vain trying to make yourself out an old woman; your figure betrays you.'

"'Years, nevertheless, have passed since I saw you, rather since you saw me, for that is what I am considering. Millarca, there, is my daughter; I cannot then be young, even in the opinion of people whom time has taught to be indulgent, and I may not like to be compared with what you remember me. You have no mask to remove. You can offer me nothing in exchange.'

"'My petition is to your pity, to remove it.'

"'And mine to yours, to let it stay where it is,' she replied.

"'Well, then, at least you will tell me whether you are French or German; you speak both languages so perfectly.'

"'I don't think I shall tell you that, General; you intend a surprise, and are meditating the particular point of attack.'

"'At all events, you won't deny this,' I said, 'that being honoured by your permission to converse, I ought to know how to address you. Shall I say Madame la Comtesse?'

"She laughed, and she would, no doubt, have met me with another evasion—if, indeed, I can treat any occurrence in an interview every circumstance of which was pre-arranged, as I now believe, with the profoundest cunning, as liable to be modified by accident.

"'As to that,' she began; but she was interrupted, almost as she opened her lips, by a gentleman, dressed in black, who looked particularly elegant and distinguished, with this drawback, that his face was the most deadly pale I ever saw, except in death. He was in no masquerade—in the plain evening dress of a gentleman; and he said, without a smile, but with a courtly and unusually low bow:

"'Will Madame la Comtesse permit me to say a very few words which may interest her?'

"The lady turned quickly to him, and touched her lip in token of silence; she then said to me, 'Keep my place for me, General; I shall return when I have said a few words.'

"And with this injunction, playfully given, she walked a little aside with the gentleman in black, and talked for some minutes, apparently very earnestly. They then walked away slowly together in the crowd, and I lost them for some minutes.

"I spent the interval in cudgelling my brains for a conjecture as to the identity of the lady who seemed to remember me so kindly, and I was thinking of turning about and joining in the conversation between my pretty ward and the Countess's daughter, and trying whether, by the time she returned, I might not have a surprise in store for her, by having her name, title, château, and estates at my fingers' ends. But at this moment she returned, accompanied by the pale man in black, who said:

"'I shall return and inform Madame la Comtesse when her carriage is at the door.'

"He withdrew with a bow."

CHAPTER XII
A PETITION

"'Then we are to lose Madame la Comtesse, but I hope only for a few hours,' I said, with a low bow.

"'It may be that only, or it may be a few weeks. It was very unlucky his speaking to me just now as he did. Do you now know me?'

"I assured her I did not.

"'You shall know me,' she said, 'but not at present. We are older and better friends than, perhaps, you suspect. I cannot yet declare myself. I shall in three weeks pass your beautiful schloss, about which I have been making inquiries. I shall then look in upon you for an hour or two, and renew a friendship which I never think of without a thousand pleasant recollections. This moment a piece of news has reached me like a thunderbolt. I must set out now, and travel by a devious route, nearly a hundred miles, with all the dispatch I can possibly make. My perplexities multiply. I am only deterred by the compulsory reserve

I practise as to my name from making a very singular request of you. My poor child has not quite recovered her strength. Her horse fell with her, at a hunt which she had ridden out to witness, her nerves have not yet recovered the shock, and our physician says that she must on no account exert herself for some time to come. We came here, in consequence, by very easy stages—hardly six leagues a day. I must now travel day and night, on a mission of life and death—a mission the critical and momentous nature of which I shall be able to explain to you when we meet, as I hope we shall, in a few weeks, without the necessity of any concealment.'

"She went on to make her petition, and it was in the tone of a person from whom such a request amounted to conferring, rather than seeking a favour. This was only in manner, and, as it seemed, quite unconsciously. Than the terms in which it was expressed, nothing could be more deprecatory. It was simply that I would consent to take charge of her daughter during her absence.

"This was, all things considered, a strange, not to say an audacious, request. She in some sort disarmed me, by stating and admitting everything that could be urged against it, and throwing herself entirely upon my chivalry. At the same moment, by a fatality that seems to have predetermined all that happened, my poor child came to my side, and, in an undertone, besought me to invite her new friend, Millarca, to pay us a visit. She had just been sounding her, and thought, if her mamma would allow her, she would like it extremely.

"At another time I should have told her to wait a little, until, at least, we knew who they were. But I had not a moment to think in. The two ladies assailed me together, and I must confess the refined and beautiful face of the young lady, about which there was something extremely engaging, as well as the elegance and fire of high birth, determined me; and, quite overpowered, I submitted, and undertook, too easily, the care of the young lady, whom her mother called Millarca.

"The Countess beckoned to her daughter, who listened with grave attention while she told her, in general terms, how suddenly and peremptorily she had been summoned, and also of the arrangement she had made for her under my care, adding that I was one of her earliest and most valued friends.

"I made, of course, such speeches as the case seemed to call for, and found myself, on reflection, in a position which I did not half like.

"The gentleman in black returned, and very ceremoniously conducted the lady from the room.

"The demeanour of this gentleman was such as to impress me with the conviction that the Countess was a lady of very much more importance than her modest title alone might have led me to assume.

"Her last charge to me was that no attempt was to be made to learn more about her than I might have already guessed, until her return. Our distinguished host, whose guest she was, knew her reasons.

"'But here,' she said, 'neither I nor my daughter could safely remain for more than a day. I removed my mask imprudently for a moment, about an hour ago, and, too late, I fancied you saw me. So I resolved to seek an opportunity of talking a little to you. Had I found that you *had* seen me, I should have thrown myself on your high sense of honour to keep my secret for some weeks. As it is, I am satisfied that you did not see me; but if you now *suspect*, or, on reflection, *should* suspect, who I am, I commit myself, in like manner, entirely to your honour. My daughter will observe the same secrecy, and I well know that you will, from time to time, remind her, lest she should thoughtlessly disclose it.'

"She whispered a few words to her daughter, kissed her hurriedly twice, and went away, accompanied by the pale gentleman in black, and disappeared in the crowd.

"'In the next room,' said Millarca, 'there is a window that looks upon the hall door. I should like to see the last of mamma, and to kiss my hand to her.'

"We assented, of course, and accompanied her to the window. We looked out, and saw a handsome old-fashioned carriage, with a troop of couriers and footmen. We saw the slim figure of the pale gentleman in black, as he held a thick velvet cloak, and placed it about her shoulders and threw the hood over her head. She nodded to him, and just touched his hand with hers. He bowed low repeatedly as the door closed, and the carriage began to move.

"'She is gone,' said Millarca, with a sigh.

"'She is gone,' I repeated to myself, for the first time—in the hurried moments that had elapsed since my consent—reflecting on the folly of my act.

"'She did not look up,' said the young lady, plaintively.

"'The Countess had taken off her mask, perhaps, and did not care to show her face,' I said; 'and she could not know that you were in the window.'

"She sighed, and looked in my face. She was so beautiful that I relented. I was sorry I had for a moment repented of my hospitality, and I determined to make amends for the unavowed churlishness of my reception.

"The young lady, replacing her mask, joined my ward in persuading me to return to the grounds, where the concert was soon to be renewed. We did so, and walked up and down the terrace that lies under the castle windows. Millarca became very intimate with us, and amused us with lively descriptions and stories of most of the great people whom we saw upon the terrace. I liked her more and more every minute. Her gossip, without being ill-natured, was extremely diverting to me, who had been so long out of the great world. I thought what life she would give to our sometimes lonely evenings at home.

"This ball was not over until the morning sun had almost reached the horizon. It pleased the Grand Duke to dance till then, so loyal people could not go away, or think of bed.

"We had just got through a crowded *salon*, when my ward asked me what had become of Millarca. I thought she had been by her side, and she fancied she was by mine. The fact was, we had lost her.

"All my efforts to find her were vain. I feared that she had mistaken, in the confusion of a momentary separation from us, other people for her new friends, and had, possibly, pursued and lost them in the extensive grounds which were thrown open to us.

"Now, in its full force, I recognized a new folly in my having undertaken the charge of a young lady without so much as knowing her name; and fettered as I was by promises, of the reasons for imposing which I knew nothing, I could not even point my inquiries by saying that the missing young lady was the daughter of the Countess who had taken her departure a few hours before.

"Morning broke. It was clear daylight before I gave up my search. It was not till near two o'clock next day that we heard anything of my missing charge.

"At about that time a servant knocked at my niece's door, to say that he had been earnestly requested by a young lady, who appeared to be in great distress, to make out where she could find the General Baron Spielsdorf and the young lady his daughter, in whose charge she had been left by her mother.

"There could be no doubt, notwithstanding the slight inaccuracy, that our young friend had turned up; and so she had. Would to heaven we had lost her!

"She told my poor child a story to account for her having failed to recover us for so long. Very late, she said, she had got to the housekeeper's bed-room in despair of finding us, and had then fallen into a deep sleep which, long as it was, had hardly sufficed to recruit her strength after the fatigues of the ball.

"That day Millarca came home with us. I was only too happy, after all, to have secured so charming a companion for my dear girl."

CHAPTER XIII
THE WOODMAN

"There soon, however, appeared some drawbacks. In the first place, Millarca complained of extreme languor—the weakness that remained after her late illness—and she never emerged from her room till the afternoon was pretty far advanced. In the next place, it was accidentally discovered, although she always locked her door on the inside, and never disturbed the key from its place till she admitted the maid to assist at her toilet, that she was undoubtedly sometimes absent from her room in the very early morning, and at various times later in the day, before she wished it to be understood that she was stirring. She was repeatedly seen from the windows of the schloss, in the first faint grey of the morning, walking through the trees, in an easterly direction, and looking like a person in a trance. This convinced me that she walked in her sleep. But this hypothesis did not solve the puzzle. How did she pass out from her room, leaving the door locked on the inside? How did she escape from the house without unbarring door or window?

"In the midst of my perplexities, an anxiety of a far more urgent kind presented itself.

"My dear child began to lose her looks and health, and that in a manner so mysterious, and even horrible, that I became thoroughly frightened.

"She was at first visited by appalling dreams; then, as she fancied, by a spectre, sometimes resembling Millarca, sometimes in the shape of a beast, indistinctly seen, walking round the foot of her bed, from side to side. Lastly came sensations. One, not unpleasant, but very peculiar, she said, resembled the flow of an icy stream against her breast. At a later time, she felt something like a pair of large needles pierce her, a little below the throat, with a very sharp pain. A few nights after followed a gradual and convulsive sense of strangulation; then came unconsciousness."

I could hear distinctly every word the kind old General was saying, because by this time we were driving upon the short grass that spreads on either side of the road as you approach the roofless village which had not shown the smoke of a chimney for more than half a century.

You may guess how strangely I felt as I heard my own symptoms so exactly described in those which had been experienced by a poor girl who, but for the catastrophe which followed, would have been at that moment a visitor at my father's château. You may suppose, also, how I felt as I heard him detail habits and mysterious peculiarities which were, in fact, those of our beautiful guest, Carmilla!

A vista opened in the forest; we were on a sudden under the chimneys and gables of the ruined village, and the towers and battlements of the dismantled castle, round which gigantic trees are grouped, overhung us from a slight eminence.

In a frightened dream I got down from the carriage,

and in silence, for we had each abundant matter for thinking; we soon mounted the ascent, and were among the spacious chambers, winding stairs, and dark corridors of the castle.

"And this was once the palatial residence of the Karnsteins!" said the old General at length, as from a great window he looked out across the village, and saw the wide, undulating expanse of forest. "It was a bad family, and here its blood-stained annals were written," he continued. "It is hard that they should, after death, continue to plague the human race with their atrocious lusts. That is the chapel of the Karnsteins, down there."

He pointed down to the grey walls of the Gothic building, partly visible through the foliage, a little way down the steep. "And I hear the axe of a woodman," he added, "busy among the trees that surround it; he possibly may give us the information of which I am in search, and point out the grave of Mircalla, Countess of Karnstein. These rustics preserve the local traditions of great families, whose stories die out among the rich and titled so soon as the families themselves become extinct."

"We have a portrait, at home, of Mircalla, the Countess Karnstein; should you like to see it?" asked my father.

"Time enough, dear friend," replied the General. "I believe that I have seen the original; and one motive which has led me to you earlier than I at first intended was to explore the chapel which we are now approaching."

"What! see the Countess Mircalla," exclaimed my father; "why, she has been dead more than a century!"

"Not so dead as you fancy, I am told," answered the General.

"I confess, General, you puzzle me utterly," replied my father, looking at him, I fancied, for a moment with a return of the suspicion I detected before. But although there was anger and detestation, at times, in the old General's manner, there was nothing flighty.

"There remains to me," he said, as we passed under the heavy arch of the Gothic church—for its dimensions would have justified its being so styled—"but one object which can interest me during the few years that remain to me on earth, and that is to wreak on her the vengeance which, I thank God, may still be accomplished by a mortal arm."

"What vengeance can you mean?" asked my father, in increasing amazement.

"I mean, to decapitate the monster," he answered, with a fierce flush, and a stamp that echoed mournfully through the hollow ruin, and his clenched hand was at the same moment raised, as if it grasped the handle of an axe, while he shook it ferociously in the air.

"What?" exclaimed my father, more than ever bewildered.

"To strike her head off."

"Cut her head off!"

"Aye, with a hatchet, with a spade, or with anything that can cleave through her murderous throat. You shall hear," he answered, trembling with rage. And hurrying forward he said:

"That beam will answer for a seat; your dear child is fatigued; let her be seated, and I will, in a few sentences, close my dreadful story."

The squared block of wood, which lay on the grass-grown pavement of the chapel, formed a bench on which I was very glad to seat myself, and in the meantime the General called to the woodman, who had been removing some boughs which leaned upon the old walls; and, axe in hand, the hardy old fellow stood before us.

He could not tell us anything of these monuments; but there was an old man, he said, a ranger of this forest, at present sojourning in the house of the priest, about two miles away, who could point out every monument of the old Karnstein family; and, for a trifle, he undertook to bring him back with him, if we would lend him one of our horses, in little more than half-an-hour.

"Have you been long employed about this forest?" asked my father of the old man.

"I have been a woodman here," he answered in his *patois*, "under the forester, all my days; so has my father before me, and so on, as many generations as I can count up. I could show you the very house in the village here, in which my ancestors lived."

"How came the village to be deserted?" asked the General.

"It was troubled by *revenants,* sir; several were tracked to their graves, there detected by the usual tests, and extinguished in the usual way, by decapitation, by the stake, and by burning; but not until many of the villagers were killed.

"But after all these proceedings according to law," he continued—"so many graves opened, and so many vampires deprived of their horrible animation—the village was not relieved. But a Moravian nobleman, who happened to be travelling this way, heard how matters were, and being skilled—as many people are in his country—in such affairs, he offered to deliver the village from its tormentor. He did so thus: There being a bright moon that night, he ascended, shortly after sunset, the tower of the chapel here, from whence he could distinctly see the churchyard beneath him; you can see it from that window. From this point he watched until he saw the vampire come out of his grave, and place near it the linen clothes in which he had been folded, and then glide away towards the village to plague its inhabitants.

"The stranger, having seen all this, came down from the steeple, took the linen wrappings of the vampire, and carried them up to the top of the tower, which he again mounted. When the vampire returned from his prowlings and missed his clothes, he cried furiously to the Moravian, whom he saw at the summit of the tower, and who, in reply, beckoned him to ascend and take them. Whereupon the vampire, accepting his invitation, began to climb the steeple, and so soon as he had reached the battlements, the Moravian, with a stroke of his sword, clove his skull in twain, hurling him down to the churchyard, whither, descending by the winding stairs, the stranger followed and cut his head off, and next day delivered it and the body to the villagers, who duly impaled and burnt them.

"This Moravian nobleman had authority from the then head of the family to remove the tomb of Mircalla, Countess Karnstein, which he did effectually, so that in a little while its site was quite forgotten."

"Can you point out where it stood?" asked the General, eagerly.

The forester shook his head and smiled.

"Not a soul living could tell you that now," he said; "besides, they say her body was removed; but no one is sure of that either."

Having thus spoken, as time pressed, he dropped his axe and departed, leaving us to hear the remainder of the General's strange story.

CHAPTER XIV
THE MEETING

"My beloved child," he resumed, "was now growing rapidly worse. The physician who attended her had failed to produce the slightest impression upon her disease, for such I then supposed it to be. He saw my alarm, and suggested a consultation. I called in an abler physician, from Gratz. Several days elapsed before he arrived. He was a good and pious, as well as a learned man. Having seen my poor ward together, they withdrew to my library to confer and discuss. I, from the adjoining room, where I awaited their summons, heard these two gentlemen's voices raised in something sharper than a strictly philosophical discussion. I knocked at the door and entered. I found the old physician from Gratz maintaining his theory. His rival was combating it with undisguised ridicule, accompanied with bursts of laugher. This unseemly manifestation subsided and the altercation ended on my entrance.

"'Sir,' said my first physician, 'my learned brother seems to think that you want a conjuror, and not a doctor.'

"'Pardon me,' said the old physician from Gratz, looking displeased, 'I shall state my own view of the case in my own way another time. I grieve, Monsieur le Général, that by my skill and science I can be of no use. Before I go I shall do myself the honour to suggest something to you.'

"He seemed thoughtful, and sat down at a table and began to write. Profoundly disappointed, I made my bow, and as I turned to go, the other doctor pointed over his shoulder to his companion who was writing, and then, with a shrug, significantly touched his forehead.

"This consultation, then, left me precisely where I was. I walked out into the grounds, all but distracted. The doctor from Gratz, in ten or fifteen minutes, overtook me. He apologized for having followed me, but said that he could not conscientiously take his leave without a few words more. He told me that he could not be mistaken; no natural disease exhibited the same symptoms; and that death was already very near. There remained, however, a day, or possibly two, of life. If the fatal seizure were at once arrested, with great care and skill her strength might possibly return. But all hung now upon the confines of the irrevocable. One more assault might extinguish the last spark of vitality which is, every moment, ready to die.

"'And what is the nature of the seizure you speak of?' I entreated.

"'I have stated all fully in this note, which I place in your hands upon the distinct condition that you send for the nearest clergyman, and open my letter in his presence, and on no account read it till he is with you; you would despise it else, and it is a matter of life and death. Should the priest fail you, then, indeed, you may read it.'

"He asked me, before taking his leave finally, whether I would wish to see a man curiously learned upon the very subject, which, after I had read his letter, would probably interest me above all others, and he urged me earnestly to invite him to visit him there; and so took his leave.

"The ecclesiastic was absent, and I read the letter by myself. At another time, or in another case, it might have excited my ridicule. But into what quackeries will not people rush for a last chance, where all accustomed means have failed, and the life of a beloved object is at stake?

"Nothing, you will say, could be more absurd than the learned man's letter. It was monstrous enough to have consigned him to a madhouse. He said that the patient was suffering from the visits of a vampire! The punctures which she described as having occurred near the throat were, he insisted, the insertion of those two long, thin, and sharp teeth which, it is well known, are peculiar to vampires; and there could be no doubt, he added, as to the well-defined presence of the small livid mark which all concurred in describing as that induced by the demon's lips, and every symptom described by the sufferer was in exact conformity with those recorded in every case of a similar visitation.

"Being myself wholly skeptical as to the existence of any such portent as the vampire, the supernatural theory of the good doctor furnished, in my opinion, but another instance of learning and intelligence oddly associated with some one hallucination. I was so miserable, however, that, rather than try nothing, I acted upon the instructions of the letter.

"I concealed myself in the dark dressing-room, that opened upon the poor patient's room, in which a candle was burning, and watched there till she was fast asleep. I stood at the door, peeping through the small crevice, my sword laid on the table beside me, as my directions prescribed, until, a little after one, I saw a large black object, very ill-defined, crawl, as it seemed to me, over the foot of the bed, and swiftly spread itself up to the poor girl's throat, where it swelled, in a moment, into a great, palpitating mass.

"For a few moments I had stood petrified. I now sprang forward, with my sword in my hand. The black creature suddenly contracted towards the foot of the bed, glided over it, and, standing on the floor about a yard below the foot of the bed, with a glare of skulking ferocity and horror fixed on me, I saw Millarca. Speculating I know not what, I struck at her instantly with my sword; but I saw her standing near the door, unscathed. Horrified, I pursued, and struck again. She was gone; and my sword flew to shivers against the door.

"I can't describe to you all that passed on that horrible night. The whole house was up and stirring. The spectre

Millarca was gone. But her victim was sinking fast, and
before the morning dawned, had died."

The old General was agitated. We did not speak to him.
My father walked to some little distance, and began reading
the inscriptions on the tombstones; and thus occupied, he
strolled into the door of a side-chapel to prosecute his
researches. The General leaned against the wall, dried his
eyes, and sighed heavily. I was relieved on hearing the
voices of Carmilla and Madame, who were at that moment
approaching. The voices died away.

In this solitude, having just listened to so strange a
story, connected, as it was, with the great and titled dead,
whose monuments were mouldering among the dust and
ivy round us, and every incident of which bore so awfully
upon my own mysterious case—in this haunted spot,
darkened by the towering foliage that rose on every side,
dense and high above its noiseless walls—a horror began
to steal over me, and my heart sank as I thought that my
friends were, after all, not about to enter and disturb this
triste and ominous scene.

The old General's eyes were fixed on the ground, as
he leaned with his hand upon the basement of a shattered
monument.

Under a narrow, arched doorway, surmounted by one
of those demoniacal grotesques in which the cynical and
ghastly fancy of old Gothic carving delights, I saw very

gladly the beautiful face and figure of Carmilla enter the shadowy chapel.

I was just about to rise and speak, and nodded smiling, in answer to her peculiarly engaging smile; when with a cry, the old man by my side caught up the woodman's hatchet, and started forward. On seeing him a brutalized change came over her features. It was an instantaneous and horrible transformation, as she made a crouching step backwards. Before I could utter a scream, he struck at her with all his force, but she dived under his blow, and unscathed, caught him in her tiny grasp by the wrist. He struggled for a moment to release his arm, but his hand opened, the axe fell to the ground, and the girl was gone.

He staggered against the wall. His grey hair stood upon his head, and a moisture shone over his face, as if he were at the point of death.

The frightful scene had passed in a moment. The first thing I recollect after is Madame standing before me, and impatiently repeating again and again the question, "Where is Mademoiselle Carmilla?"

I answered at length, "I don't know—I can't tell—she went there," and I pointed to the door through which Madame had just entered; "only a minute or two since."

"But I have been standing there, in the passage, ever since Mademoiselle Carmilla entered; and she did not return."

She then began to call "Carmilla," through every door and passage and from the windows, but no answer came.

"She called herself Carmilla?" asked the General, still agitated.

"Carmilla, yes," I answered.

"Aye," he said; "that is Millarca. That is the same person who long ago was called Mircalla, Countess Karnstein. Depart from this accursed ground, my poor child, as quickly as you can. Drive to the clergyman's house, and stay there till we come. Begone! May you never behold Carmilla more; you will not find her here."

CHAPTER XV

ORDEAL AND EXECUTION

As he spoke one of the strangest-looking men I ever beheld entered the chapel at the door through which Carmilla had made her entrance and her exit. He was tall, narrow-chested, stooping, with high shoulders, and dressed in black. His face was brown and dried in with deep furrows; he wore an oddly-shaped hat with a broad leaf. His hair, long and grizzled, hung on his shoulders. He wore a pair of gold spectacles, and walked slowly, with an odd shambling gait, with his face sometimes turned up to the sky, and sometimes bowed down towards the ground,

and seemed to wear a perpetual smile; his long thin arms
were swinging, and his lank hands, in old black gloves
ever so much too wide for them, waving and gesticulating
in utter abstraction.

"The very man!" exclaimed the General, advancing
with manifest delight. "My dear Baron, how happy I am
to see you, I had no hope of meeting you so soon." He
signed to my father, who had by this time returned, leading
the fantastic old gentleman, whom he called the Baron,
to meet him. He introduced him formally, and they at
once entered into earnest conversation. The stranger took
a roll of paper from his pocket, and spread it on the
worn surface of a tomb that stood by. He had a pencil
case in his fingers, with which he traced imaginary lines
from point to point on the paper, which from their often
glancing from it, together, at certain points of the building,
I concluded to be a plan of the chapel. He accompanied,
what I may term his lecture, with occasional readings
from a dirty little book, whose yellow leaves were closely
written over.

They sauntered together down the aisle, opposite to the
spot where I was standing, conversing as they went; then
they began measuring distances by paces, and finally they
all stood together, facing a piece of the side-wall, which
they began to examine with great minuteness; pulling off
the ivy that clung over it, and rapping the plaster with the

ends of their sticks, scraping here, and knocking there. At length they ascertained the existence of a broad marble tablet, with letters carved in relief upon it.

With the assistance of the woodman, who soon returned, a monumental inscription, and carved escutcheon, were disclosed. They proved to be those of the long lost monument of Mircalla, Countess Karnstein.

The old General, though not I fear given to the praying mood, raised his hands and eyes to heaven, in mute thanksgiving for some moments.

"To-morrow," I heard him say; "the commissioner will be here, and the Inquisition will be held according to law."

Then turning to the old man with the gold spectacles, whom I have described, he shook him warmly by both hands and said:

"Baron, how can I thank you? How can we all thank you? You will have delivered this region from a plague that has scourged its inhabitants for more than a century. The horrible enemy, thank God, is at last tracked."

My father led the stranger aside, and the General followed. I knew that he had led them out of hearing, that he might relate my case, and I saw them glance often quickly at me, as the discussion proceeded.

My father came to me, kissed me again and again, and leading me from the chapel, said:

"It is time to return, but before we go home, we must add to our party the good priest, who lives but a little way from this; and persuade him to accompany us to the schloss."

In this quest we were successful: and I was glad, being unspeakably fatigued when we reached home. But my satisfaction was changed to dismay, on discovering that there were no tidings of Carmilla. Of the scene that had occurred in the ruined chapel, no explanation was offered to me, and it was clear that it was a secret which my father for the present determined to keep from me.

The sinister absence of Carmilla made the remembrance of the scene more horrible to me. The arrangements for that night were singular. Two servants and Madame were to sit up in my room that night; and the ecclesiastic with my father kept watch in the adjoining dressing-room.

The priest had performed certain solemn rites that night, the purport of which I did not understand any more than I comprehended the reason of this extraordinary precaution taken for my safety during sleep.

I saw all clearly a few days later.

The disappearance of Carmilla was followed by the discontinuance of my nightly sufferings.

You have heard, no doubt, of the appalling superstition that prevails in Upper and Lower Styria, in Moravia, Silesia, in Turkish Servia, in Poland, even in Russia; the superstition, so we must call it, of the vampire.

If human testimony, taken with every care and
solemnity, judicially, before commissions innumerable,
each consisting of many members, all chosen for integrity
and intelligence, and constituting reports more voluminous
perhaps than exist upon any one other class of cases, is
worth anything, it is difficult to deny, or even to doubt the
existence of such a phenomenon as the vampire.

For my part I have heard no theory by which to
explain what I myself have witnessed and experienced,
other than that supplied by the ancient and well-attested
belief of the country.

The next day the formal proceedings took place in the
Chapel of Karnstein. The grave of the Countess Mircalla
was opened; and the General and my father recognized
each his perfidious and beautiful guest, in the face now
disclosed to view. The features, though a hundred and
fifty years had passed since her funeral, were tinted with
the warmth of life. Her eyes were open; no cadaverous
smell exhaled from the coffin. The two medical men, one
officially present, the other on the part of the promoter
of the inquiry, attested the marvellous fact, that there was
a faint but appreciable respiration, and a corresponding
action of the heart. The limbs were perfectly flexible, the
flesh elastic; and the leaden coffin floated with blood, in
which to a depth of seven inches, the body lay immersed.

Here, then, were all the admitted signs and proofs of vampirism. The body, therefore, in accordance with the ancient practice, was raised, and a sharp stake driven through the heart of the vampire, who uttered a piercing shriek at the moment, in all respects such as might escape from a living person in the last agony. Then the head was struck off, and a torrent of blood flowed from the severed neck. The body and head were next placed on a pile of wood, and reduced to ashes, which were thrown upon the river and borne away, and that territory has never since been plagued by the visits of a vampire.

My father has a copy of the report of the Imperial Commission, with the signatures of all who were present at these proceedings, attached in verification of the statement. It is from this official paper that I have summarized my account of this last shocking scene.

CHAPTER XVI
CONCLUSION

I write all this you suppose with composure. But far from it; I cannot think of it without agitation. Nothing but your earnest desire so repeatedly expressed could have induced me to sit down to a task that has unstrung my nerves for months to come, and re-induced a shadow of the unspeakable horror which years after my deliverance continued to make my days and nights dreadful, and solitude insupportably terrific.

Let me add a word or two about that quaint Baron Vordenburg, to whose curious lore we were indebted for the discovery of the Countess Mircalla's grave.

He had taken up his abode in Gratz, where, living upon a mere pittance, which was all that remained to him of the once princely estates of his family, in Upper Styria, he devoted himself to the minute and laborious investigation of the marvellously authenticated tradition of vampirism. He had at his fingers' ends all the great and little works upon the subject: "Magia Posthuma," "Phlegon de Mirabilibus," "Augustinus de curâ pro Mortuis," "Philosophicae et Christianae Cogitationes de Vampiris," by John Christofer Harenberg; and a thousand others, among which I remember only a few of those which he lent to my father. He had a voluminous digest of all the judicial cases, from which he had extracted a system of principles that appear to govern—some always, and others occasionally only—the condition of the vampire. I may mention, in passing, that the deadly pallor attributed to that sort of *revenants* is a mere melodramatic fiction. They present, in the grave, and when they show themselves in human society, the appearance of healthy life. When disclosed to light in their coffins, they exhibit all the symptoms that are enumerated as those which proved the vampire-life of the long-dead Countess Karnstein.

How they escape from their graves and return to them for certain hours every day, without displacing the clay or leaving any trace of disturbance in the state of the coffin or the cerements, has always been admitted to be utterly inexplicable. The amphibious existence of the vampire is sustained by daily renewed slumber in the grave. Its horrible lust for living blood supplies the vigour of its waking existence. The vampire is prone to be fascinated with an engrossing vehemence, resembling the passion of love, by particular persons. In pursuit of these it will exercise inexhaustible patience and stratagem, for access to a particular object may be obstructed in a hundred ways. It will never desist until it has satiated its passion, and drained the very life of its coveted victim. But it will, in these cases, husband and protract its murderous enjoyment with the refinement of an epicure, and heighten it by the gradual approaches of an artful courtship. In these cases it seems to yearn for something like sympathy and consent. In ordinary ones it goes direct to its object, overpowers with violence, and strangles and exhausts often at a single feast.

The vampire is, apparently, subject, in certain situations, to special conditions. In the particular instance of which I have given you a relation, Mircalla seemed to be limited to a name which, if not her real one, should at least reproduce, without the omission or addition of a single letter, those, as we say, anagrammatically, which compose it. *Carmilla* did this; so did *Millarca*.

My father related to the Baron Vordenburg, who remained with us for two or three weeks after the expulsion of Carmilla, the story about the Moravian nobleman and the vampire at Karnstein churchyard, and then he asked the Baron how he had discovered the exact position of the long-concealed tomb of the Countess Millarca? The Baron's grotesque features puckered up into a mysterious smile; he looked down, still smiling, on his worn spectacle-case and fumbled with it. Then looking up, he said:

"I have many journals, and other papers, written by that remarkable man; the most curious among them is one treating of the visit of which you speak, to Karnstein. The tradition, of course, discolours and distorts a little. He might have been termed a Moravian nobleman, for he had changed his abode to that territory, and was, beside, a noble. But he was, in truth, a native of Upper Styria. It is enough to say that in very early youth he had been a passionate and favoured lover of the beautiful Mircalla, Countess Karnstein. Her early death plunged him into inconsolable grief. It is the nature of vampires to increase and multiply, but according to an ascertained and ghostly law.

"Assume, at starting, a territory perfectly free from that

pest. How does it begin, and how does it multiply itself? I will tell you. A person, more or less wicked, puts an end to himself. A suicide, under certain circumstances, becomes a vampire. That spectre visits living people in their slumbers; *they* die, and almost invariably, in the grave, develop into vampires. This happened in the case of the beautiful Mircalla, who was haunted by one of those demons. My ancestor, Vordenburg, whose title I still bear, soon discovered this, and in the course of the studies to which he devoted himself, learned a great deal more.

"Among other things, he concluded that suspicion of vampirism would probably fall, sooner or later, upon the dead Countess, who in life had been his idol. He conceived a horror, be she what she might, of her remains being profaned by the outrage of a posthumous execution. He has left a curious paper to prove that the vampire, on its expulsion from its amphibious existence, is projected into a far more horrible life; and he resolved to save his once beloved Mircalla from this.

"He adopted the stratagem of a journey here, a pretended removal of her remains, and a real obliteration of her monument. When age had stolen upon him, and from the vale of years he looked back on the scenes he was leaving, he considered, in a different spirit, what he had done, and a horror took possession of him. He made the tracings and notes which have guided me to the very

spot, and drew up a confession of the deception that he
had practised. If he had intended any further action in this
matter, death prevented him; and the hand of a remote
descendant has, too late for many, directed the pursuit to
the lair of the beast."

We talked a little more, and among other things he said
was this:

"One sign of the vampire is the power of the hand. The
slender hand of Mircalla closed like a vice of steel on the
General's wrist when he raised the hatchet to strike. But its
power is not confined to grasp; it leaves a numbness in the
limb it seizes, which is slowly, if ever, recovered from."

The following Spring my father took me on a tour
through Italy. We remained away for more than a year. It
was long before the terror of recent events subsided; and
to this hour the image of Carmilla returns to the memory
with ambiguous alternations—sometimes the playful,
languid, beautiful girl; sometimes the writhing fiend I saw
in the ruined church; and often from a reverie I have
started, fancying I heard the light step of Carmilla at the
drawing-room door.